A 'HOUSE UPON A ROCK

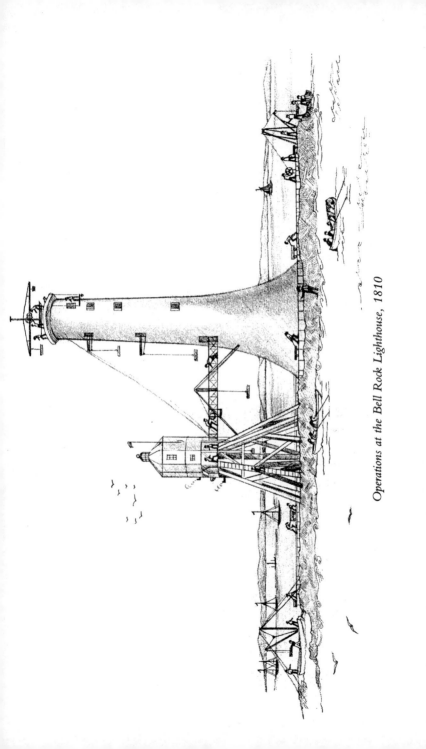

Operations at the Bell Rock Lighthouse, 1810

A 'HOUSE UPON A ROCK

– the story of the building of the Bell Rock Lighthouse

Kathryn L. Moore

Illustrated by Wendy Campbell

LANDSBOROUGH BOOKS

Published in 1997 by
LANDSBOROUGH BOOKS
7 Allathan Park, Pitmedden, Ellon, Aberdeenshire,
AB41 7PX

Text copyright ©Kathryn L. Moore 1997
Illustrations copyright ©Wendy Campbell 1997
All Rights Reserved

British Library Cataloguing in Publication Data
A catalogue record for this book is available from the British
Library
ISBN No. 0 9529083 0 1
Printed in Great Britain by
Printagraph Ltd., 12 Berryden Road, Aberdeen.

To
all those (in the past or the present)
who have helped turn a dream
into reality

Acknowledgements

I am most grateful to the Northern Lighthouse Board for information which brought the story of the Bell Rock Lighthouse up to date and to the RNLI (Arbroath Branch) for further details of the evacuation of the lighthouse after the fire there in 1987. The many Arbroath folk who shared their memories of the lighthouse with me when I lived in the town are also due my thanks as is Wendy Campbell for providing the perfect illustrations for the book.

The most important thank you of all, however, should perhaps go to the men who actually built the Bell Rock Lighthouse (and others). Although frequently risking their own lives in the process, they rose to the challenge which faced them. In doing so they not only made travel by sea safer but also gave us a remarkable story of courage and ingenuity.

CONTENTS

ILLUSTRATIONS

THE EAST COAST OF SCOTLAND

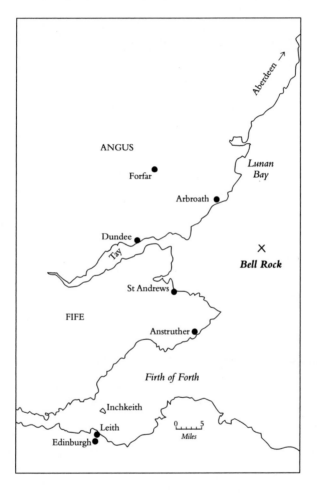

PREFACE

In his book *Remarks on Scotland,* which was published in 1801, John Stoddart mentioned an old account from the first half of the seventeenth century. The story went as follows:-

"By east of the Isle of May, twelve miles from all land in the Germayne Seas, lye a great hidden rock, called Inchcape, very dangerous for navigators, because it is overflowed everie tide. It is reported, in old times, upon the said rocke there was a bell, fixed upon a tree or timber, which rang continually, being moved by the sea, giving notice to the saylers of the danger. This bell or clocke was put there and maintained by the Abbot of Aberbrothok, and being taken down by a sea pirate, a yeare thereafter he perished upon the same rocke with ship and goods, in the righteous judgement of God."

Some piracy did take place along the Scottish coast in earlier centuries, with local and foreign seamen preying on vessels. In times of war, the capture of foreign vessels was considered quite legitimate. This practice continued into the nineteenth century and privateers frequently had a serious effect on the trade of the east coast ports.

CHAPTER ONE

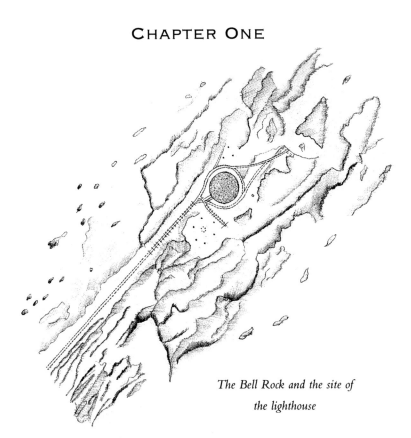

*The Bell Rock and the site of
the lighthouse*

IN THE BEGINNING ...

It was not fair. IT WAS JUST NOT FAIR!

Michael stared miserably out of the window of his grandfather's house at Arbroath.

The problem was the rain; rain which at that very moment was lashing against the glass of the window panes. To make matters worse, it had been like that for hours.

It had been bright and sunny the day before. Michael's father had driven him across to stay for a few days on his own with his grandfather and the first few raindrops had only begun to fall while Michael and his grandfather waved good-bye. As the sky darkened they became heavier and heavier. Not for a single moment since then had any break in the clouds looked likely. On the contrary, it continued to rain as if it had never rained before.

The boy searched desperately for any sign that it might be about to clear. It was all to no purpose. He could barely see the end of the garden.

In the distance he could hear a *booming* noise which he knew was the sound of the sea breaking fiercely over the harbour wall. He had seen it many times before. It had been fun to watch the spray rise high into the air and then fall down onto the stonework of the quay, soaking everything within reach.

Well, he did not appreciate it now! Why, oh why did the weather have to be bad on this, his first holiday by himself with his grandfather?

Michael had been so excited about the prospect. Little else had occupied his mind for the last few weeks. There had been so many things he had thought they could do together. And, now that he was here, the weather was dreadful and the rain could do nothing but pour down!

Totally fed up, he turned round and collapsed into one of the chairs beside the fire. As he did so he knocked over the pile of games that had been slowly accumulating on the floor all morning. Some chess pieces fell out and rolled across the carpet. He made no effort to pick them up although he knew his grandfather would insist upon it later on.

He gave a deep sigh, for effect as much as anything, and let his eyes wander around the room he loved so well. Nothing ever seemed to change here.

There was the old clock on the wall, the ship in a bottle, the Sunderland ware bowl on the table and his grandfather's books. Few of the names meant much to Michael but they were all well worn and had obviously been read and re-read on many occasions.

For the first time the boy really took notice of a piece of stone which held some of them in place. It was not like a proper bookend. Instead it was of rough rock, red in colour like the cliffs to the north of the town.

He lifted it down to look at it more closely. From experience he had discovered that there was a story behind most of his grandfather's possessions. Why on earth would he keep this?

At that moment his grandfather appeared carrying a tray with two mugs of hot tea and a plate of biscuits. As he put it down on the footstool Michael asked 'Why do you keep this stone, Grandad?'

'Oh, it came from the Bell Rock,' he replied, sitting down in his chair. 'When they were building the lighthouse they used to bring back the chippings of stone from the Rock as ballast. Lots of folk kept a piece as a momento and a few, like that one, were kept from generation to generation. Had it been today I suppose someone would have sold them off and made a small fortune.'

While his grandfather took a mouthful of tea, Michael examined the piece of rock in his hand, feeling its texture with his fingers. At night, if the weather was clear, he could see the lighthouse from the bedroom upstairs. Its beam flashed far out at sea. Twelve miles offshore to be exact. Regular. Dependable. Strong. Permanent.

He had never really thought about what it must have been like before the lighthouse had been built to mark the position of the infamous Bell Rock.

One thing he did know was that the sandstone reef in question had also been referred to in the past as the Inchcape Rock. On one of his grandfather's old maps he had even seen it called just the *Scape*.

Michael had often heard, too, the story of Sir Ralph the Rover associated with the Bell Rock. According to the local tradition, an Abbot of Arbroath Abbey placed a bell on the Rock to warn ships of the dangerous reef nearby. However Sir Ralph (a pirate who once frequented that part of the coast) cut away the warning bell in the hope of collecting plunder from any ships which were wrecked there afterwards. In the end he, himself, was drowned along with his crew when his own vessel ran aground on the Inchcape Rock.

Michael's grandfather, however, had always stressed that it was all just a tale. In the old abbey records no evidence had ever been found to suggest that any abbot had actually ordered such a bell to be placed there.

If that part of the story was not strictly true, then Michael found himself wondering if the Rock itself had been as much of a hazard as everyone made out. He said as much to his grandfather.

'Oh it was dangerous, Michael, very dangerous indeed. No-one over the centuries has ever doubted that fact.

'Although the Rock is quite narrow it is over four hundred metres long. Its surface is rough and irregular and can be covered by anything up to five metres of water at high tide. Yet to look at it then, there is not so much as a ripple to suggest what lies just underneath.

'That was the danger. It was all too easy for a ship to hit the Rock before an unsuspecting crew realised that it was close at hand.

'What made matters worse was that the Rock lies directly in the path of any shipping heading for the Forth or Tay estuaries. There has always been a lot of trading done in these parts so the Rock was a major problem.

'Today's vessels have powerful engines and modern equipment such as radar. Two hundred years ago, seamen had to rely on canvas sails and navigate by the sun or stars. They had to be very, very careful if they were sailing along this part of the coast.'

'So people really were scared by it?'

'Very much so! In fact it was said that fear of the Rock wrecked as many, if not more ships than the Rock itself. In a bad storm, many sailors preferred to take their chance out at sea rather than risk running for the shelter of a harbour if they knew there was a chance of them being driven towards the Rock. Inevitably some of those vessels sank or were wrecked further along the coast.'

'Then when exactly did they build the lighthouse?' asked Michael.

'At the beginning of the nineteenth century. It had been talked about before then but the problems of building a lighthouse in such a location were enormous. No-one knew if it could even be done.

'The only lighthouse to have successfully withstood the sea in a similar situation was the one on the Eddystone Rock off the south coast of England. It had been designed by John Smeaton and built with stone. But although the Eddystone light had been completed in 1759 and posed its own problems, the Eddystone Rock had not been covered by as much water as was to be found at high tide out on the Bell Rock.'

'So what did make them go ahead?'

'In the end, public pressure. The country had changed a great deal over the second half of the eighteenth century and had become a lot wealthier. The Bell Rock was a threat to that prosperity.

'There were many still alive, if you just think about it, who could remember the battle of Culloden and the '45

Rebellion. It was very much the same as my being able to remember the end of the Second World War.

'Just as our world has changed since then with computers, men going into space and other such things, so a lot of new developments took place in the more peaceful years which followed Bonnie Prince Charlie's defeat.

'There were the improvements in farming techniques, for example, which are now referred to as the agricultural revolution. And there was the beginning of the industrial revolution as well, with new ideas and inventions.

'Hereabouts we had the growth of the flax and jute industries. In Arbroath itself, new mills were built along the Brothock burn and bleachfields were laid out. But all over the country there were new products to export and raw materials to be imported.

'Trade increased greatly, not only with our old trading partners across the North Sea but also with the new colonies which were opening up. Most harbours around the coast were busy and a lot of new ships were built to help carry the extra business.

'You must remember that there were no railways at the time and road conditions in most areas were still poor. The building of new toll roads to link many Scottish towns and villages had only begun and much remained to be done over the next hundred years through the work of people like Thomas Telford and John McAdam.

'At the period we are speaking of even fuel and other

necessities were usually brought in by sea. Ships were a lot smaller then than they are today and they could call in at Arbroath or any other town which possessed a harbour.

'People, too, quite often travelled by sea if they were heading for places like Aberdeen or London. For many it was the most convenient way.'

Michael's grandfather paused for a moment to take another sip of tea. He noticed that only one biscuit remained on the plate and made a mental note to put out a smaller selection next time.

His grandson was still busy eating but was no longer lounging in the chair. Instead, he was sitting cross-legged, his elbows resting on his knees and his head cupped in his hands.

The rain was forgotten. Michael's imagination was already in the past waiting for his grandfather to continue...

'All this extra traffic at sea inevitably highlighted the dangers to be found there. Not just here but all around the coast. The location of the few lighthouses which did exist at that time tended to be rather haphazard and they belonged to different people. Many felt that a more organised set-up was required.

'One of those who pressed hard for something to be done was an Angus man, George Dempster of Dunnichen. His estate lay less than ten miles from Arbroath, towards the town of Forfar. Like many men of the period he was not only a landowner but also a lawyer and a Member of Parliament. Furthermore, he was active in the agricultural reforms of the time and laid out a new village called Letham on his land. There, he encouraged the development of linen weaving.

'In 1786 George Dempster was involved in bringing an Act before Parliament which led to the setting up of a board of trustees whose job it would be to build lighthouses in Scotland. These, it was hoped, would make sailing a lot safer.

'This new body - the Commissioners of Northern Lights - was mainly composed of representatives from local authorities (such as lord provosts or provosts) and those who held high positions in the legal profession (the sheriffs of various counties). The Lord Advocate and the Solicitor General for Scotland were also included.

'The first task they were given was to build four lighthouses. One was to be at Kinnaird Head near Fraserburgh, one on the Orkney island of North Ronaldsay, one on Scalpay in the Outer Hebrides and the last at the Mull of Kintyre.

'But in beginning to build the lighthouses, they were moving into a new area in which no-one possessed all the requisite knowledge. The Board therefore advertised for assistance from anyone who could be of help.

'One man who came forward was called Thomas Smith. Born near Dundee, he was the son and grandson of ships' captains but as his father had died young, Thomas was sent instead to serve an apprenticeship as a tinsmith.

An important part of their trade was the manufacture of oil lamps.

'Thomas Smith later moved to Edinburgh and set up in business for himself, experimenting with lamps to improve their performance. His expertise in this field was obviously an important asset as far as the lights for the lighthouses were concerned. In due course he became the Lighthouse Board's first engineer.

'A further offer of help came from a Mr. Ezekiel Walker of King's Lynn in England. He said that for a sum of fifty guineas (£52.50) he would either build one lighthouse for the Board (which they could then use as a pattern) or he would instruct whoever the Board cared to send to him in all he knew about the building of lighthouses.

'Thomas Smith was sent south to glean what information he could and the rest of the job of engineer he more or less learned as he went along. However this was a time when men often worked in several different fields.

'The first of the four lighthouses to come into operation was the one at Kinnaird Head near Fraserburgh. There, the Commissioners bought an old sixteenth century castle from its owner, Lord Saltoun, and built a lantern on top. It was lit for the first time on the 1st December, 1787.

'The other three lighthouses followed and once they were in operation, any ships passing them were charged a fee of one penny per register ton if they were British, and

IN THE BEGINNING ...

tuppence (2d) if they were foreign. Now sixpence in old money was the equivalent of two and a half pence today because there were then 240 pennies in every £1. The amount charged may not seem a lot in modern terms but it was a reasonable rate for the time.

'No-one objected to the extra cost. Sea journeys were made easier by the presence of the lights and the money which was collected enabled the Lighthouse Board both to maintain them and to build new ones. The demand for more lights was such that by 1789 the Commissioners' authority had been extended to cover the whole of the Scottish coast.

'As the work load increased, Thomas Smith asked Robert Stevenson (the son of a family friend) to join his firm as an apprentice. It was soon evident that the young man possessed a great deal of talent and before long he was working on lighthouse projects under his employer.

'In the event, they were not merely to remain as employer and employee. Thomas Smith married Stevenson's widowed mother and some years later Robert Stevenson married Jane Smith, Thomas Smith's daughter from an earlier marriage.

'Robert Stevenson became a partner in the business and gradually took on more and more responsibility in relation to the building of new lighthouses. For a number of years both men acted as Engineers to the Lighthouse Board but when Thomas Smith finally retired from those duties, Robert Stevenson took over as their sole engineer.

'The enormous success of all the new lighthouses inevitably led to a discussion about the possibility of building one on the Bell Rock. However the task remained a daunting one and the cost was far more than the Commissioners could afford from the money which they, themselves, were able to raise. So, for a time, nothing happened.

'Then, at the end of 1799, there began a series of disastrous storms. Over seventy vessels were thought to have been stranded or lost around the Scottish coast. Many people believed that some of them might have been saved had there been a light on the Bell Rock. From the number of lives lost and the cost in terms of goods and shipping, it was clear that marking the Bell Rock was not just a matter of local importance, as some had suggested, but was vital for the sake of the whole country.

'This fact was brought home further when a naval ship, HMS York, was lost while in the area a few years later. She was thought by many to have foundered on the Bell Rock although the incident may actually have occurred further north along the coast. What is not in doubt is the fact that all on board were lost – almost five hundred men.

'Some ideas for a beacon on the Rock were put forward by various individuals. One, designed by a Captain Brodie and a Mr. Joseph Cooper of Leith, was even erected there. Although made of cast iron, it was washed away before long.

'By this time it seemed quite clear that only a stone

lighthouse similar to the Eddystone light would be strong enough to withstand the fierce conditions of the North Sea in winter and only the Commissioners of Northern Lights could oversee the construction of such a difficult and expensive undertaking.

'Robert Stevenson visited the Bell Rock several times and he was convinced that the project was perfectly feasible. What they still found very difficult to do was to raise the finance to pay for it. The surplus money which the Board had available each year was around £2000 - nowhere near the kind of sum required to build a lighthouse in such a difficult location. Furthermore there were other sites on the Scottish mainland that also needed attention. It was decided, therefore, to ask the Government for help.

'Their first plans and a request for a loan were laid before Parliament in 1803 with the security for the loan being the lighthouse dues that would be raised. However there was opposition to the scheme from some sources and in the end the Bill had to be withdrawn.

'Before going back to Parliament a second time, the Commissioners approached a man called John Rennie for further advice. He was another Scot, born in East Lothian, and a well known civil engineer based in London. Over the years he was responsible for a number of important harbour works, bridges and canals. The Northern Lighthouse Board asked him to act as their consultant on the project.

'Rennie agreed with Stevenson that a stone lighthouse was the only practical possibility. So, in 1806, plans for a lighthouse on the Bell Rock were once again brought before Parliament. The estimated cost was £45,134.75 (a very large amount for those days) and the sum required from the Government was £25,000.

'Even on this occasion obtaining the loan seemed to be in doubt right up until the last moment. But by now the weight of public opinion behind the project was enormous. Famous people of the time and many port authorities were among those who added their support to the venture.

'In the end, on the 16th July 1806, the Bill granting the necessary finance was finally passed by Parliament.

'Work on building the lighthouse could actually begin!'

CHAPTER TWO

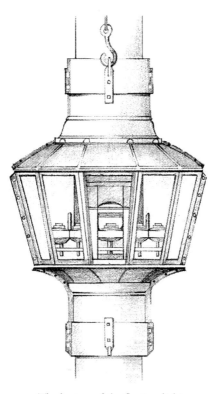

The lantern of the floating light

THE PREPARATORY WORK

'Needless to say everyone was jubilant at the passing of the Bill. But for those who now had to turn the plans into reality, the task ahead was gigantic.

'No matter how confident they were that the work could be done successfully, there must have been moments when they wondered if they had bitten off more than they could chew. After all, no-one else had ever tried to build a lighthouse so far from land on a rock which was uncovered only at low tide. And sometimes not even then!

'The first tasks that had to be undertaken were to gather together all the equipment and materials required for the building operations. Plans and drawings also had to be finalised. It was only possible to begin organising these aspects once the government loan had been secured and inevitably that was going to take some time. As a result, the actual building work on the Rock could not begin straight away. The Bill had been passed in July 1806 but any operations on the Rock were going to have to wait until the following year.

'Over the winter they knew that the weather and sea would be much too rough to allow anything to be done there. Construction work could only go ahead during the summer months when weather conditions would, hopefully, be better and they would have the advantage of the long daylight hours. All they could do in the meantime was get as far ahead as possible with the preparatory work.

'Their first priority, anyway, was not the lighthouse itself but to mark the position of the Rock temporarily. In the Bill that had gone through Parliament there had been a clause which allowed the Lighthouse Board to charge dues once that had been done. This was important because it meant that the Board could raise much needed finance from ships passing the Bell Rock even before the lighthouse had actually been built.

'For British ships the charge was one and a half (old) pence per register ton and as usual foreign ships paid twice that amount. It was, however, intended to reduce this cost by half once the lighthouse was in operation. That, it was thought, could take anything up to seven years. It might be possible to plan the construction work to the finest detail but no-one could control the wind and weather.

'The site of the Rock was to be marked in two ways. First of all a large wooden beacon was to be fixed to the Rock itself. This would show its location in daylight as it would be tall enough to appear above sea level no matter how high the tide. In addition, a floating light was to be anchored nearby for use at night. It would be visible in the dark to any passing vessels.

'For the floating light they needed a ship on which lanterns could be lit each evening. The choice of vessel was very important because she was going to have to remain at anchor for a number of years without once returning to shore. Not only that, she would also have to be strong enough to withstand any gale that the North Sea might throw at her.

'At this point in time Britain was at war with France and Napoleon controlled much of Europe. This fact was to have a bearing on the building work in several ways over the years it was in progress. The first occasion was in the search for a suitable ship for the floating light.

'A lot of skirmishes went on between British and enemy shipping in the North Sea. Foreign vessels were sometimes captured and then sold. One of these, Prussian in origin, was purchased to act as the lightship.

'The vessel's shape was important in that she had a flat bottom and was rounded off at both stem and stern. It was hoped that this would make her very buoyant and yet stable enough for the job in hand. The ship was in need of a refit, however, to make her suitable for the work ahead and so she went into Leith docks where her rigging was altered and various other changes were made.

'They decided to rename the ship the *Pharos* after the famous lighthouse at Alexandria, one of the seven wonders of the ancient world. Eighty three tons in size, she was a little under nineteen metres long but inevitably, because of her shape, she did not have a deep hold. In fact it was less than two and a half metres deep.

'Nevertheless, once she was in position at the Rock it was also intended to use the *Pharos* as an extra base on which some of the lighthouse workmen could live. Their work would inevitably come to a halt with each high tide. So, in addition to the berths required for her thirteen man crew, an extra thirty were provided for use (when necessary) by the workmen.

'The lights fitted to the *Pharos* were quite interesting. In those days anything of this nature was usually provided by suspending lanterns either from the yards or from another part of the ship. That was impractical in the conditions which the *Pharos* was likely to meet as the lamps would tend to sway with the motion of the ship. Any damage done to even one of them would bring with it the great risk of a fire on board. And, if the light was to be extinguished completely, a passing vessel might be lulled into a false sense of security.

'What they did instead was attach a copper lantern to all three of the ship's masts. However each lantern was constructed in such a way that the centre was hollow and so the mast was able to run up through the middle of it.

'Each lantern consisted of ten oil lamps, set in a circular pattern. Every lamp had a silver plated reflector and, just like the old oil lamps at home, they had to be filled with oil and have the wicks trimmed regularly.

'Although the lanterns could be moved for any maintenance required, there was no way that they could be removed or detached from the masts themselves. They were as secure as anyone could make them. And when the lamps were all lit, an uninterrupted beam of light was produced which could be seen from all directions.

'To make the lightship even more distinctive, the lantern on the central mast was fixed over two metres higher than those on the other masts. So, for a ship out at sea they made a very definite pattern, easily identifiable. From the side, the lights formed the shape of a triangle but from anywhere else it appeared as if one light was on top of the other.

'By day, the *Pharos* flew the flag of the lighthouse service. It was a blue flag with a lighthouse on it. She was also provided with a bell which could be tolled if the weather turned foggy. When required it was rung at regular one minute intervals, day or night.

'Getting the *Pharos* ready took until July of the next year, 1807, but on the 9th of that month she began her journey to the Bell Rock. Although it was the middle of summer, poor weather delayed her anchoring when she arrived. Nevertheless, after some discussion with those who knew the area well, she was eventually moored one and a half miles north-west of the Rock.

'Even that procedure did not go too smoothly. At the first attempt the anchor went down so fast that it carried the full length of chain with it and everything had to be fished up from the bottom!

'Despite the worry caused by the incident, the *Pharos* was finally secured and for a few weeks she lay at anchor so that everyone could see how she performed. The plan was that if all went well it would then be possible to advertise in the newspapers the date from which the floating light would officially operate.

'No major problems were found. The only nasty moment to occur was when the *Pharos* broke free from her moorings after a bad storm. It was realised that if the ship had done this during the storm itself she, too, might have ended up on the Rock.

'Clearly her location needed to be altered slightly. Once

the sails had been set to bring her back, those in charge decided it would be better to anchor one mile to the south-west of her previous position. After that everything went smoothly and on the 15th September the floating light shone out, officially, for the first time.

'While work on preparing the Pharos was going ahead, plans were also moving forward in other matters. It was hoped that over the summer of 1807 it would be possible to build the beacon which would mark the site of the Rock by day until the lighthouse itself had been completed.

'Although John Rennie and Robert Stevenson continued to write to one another about the building operations, the task of supervising the actual work on site fell to Stevenson. Over the early months of 1807 he went back to the Rock several times in order to see to some preparatory work. Peter Logan (who was to be the foreman builder) and several other workmen went with him.

'They began to get to know the Rock well and to understand what the likely problems were going to be. The sandstone reef was long and narrow, running approximately north-east to south-west. Its surface was very rough but there were inlets which could be used by rowing boats to reach the main area of rock. Even at low tide it was only the topmost part of the rock surface which was uncovered. The highest point lay towards the north-east but the area available for building on measured only a hundred and twenty eight metres by seventy metres. When it was possible to stand there other pieces of the reef could be seen round about, jutting above the level of the water and giving the appearance of tiny islands.

'On the rock surface there were a lot of ledges, formed by the constant action of the sea. In due course the men gave names to many of these and to other parts of the Rock, names which often related to people or events associated with the work. There was *Port Rennie,* for example, as well as *Port Stevenson, Sir Ralph the Rover's Ledge, Smith's Rock, Logan's Reach* and an island called *Peter Fortune.*

'Not unnaturally, the surface of the rock was covered in seaweed. They had to clear some of this to mark out on the sandstone the sites for the beacon and the lighthouse. Later on, when the construction work began, the seaweed proved to have a medicinal use. A number of the men who were badly affected by sea sickness ate some of it in an attempt to settle their stomachs.

'As they got on with preparing what they could on the Rock, the men found that a lot of seabirds landed there at low tide, possibly because of the fish and shellfish round about. There were even seals nearby and as many as fifty or sixty were counted at different times. Sadly, over the months which followed they were scared away by all the activity. Some of the workers took an interest in the way the fish swam around the Rock and in time the men insisted that they could forecast weather conditions from the way the fish behaved.

'Everyone was aware that the state of the tide would determine how much work could be done each day. Each month, at the time of the spring tides there was the greatest range between the high and low water marks. The area where the lighthouse was to be built was then approximately 3.7 metres below the high water mark and 1.2 metres above the low water mark.

'At the time of the neap tides, however, the level of the sea did not vary as much. The Rock was barely visible then, even at low tide. It was only going to be possible to work when the level of the sea was low enough for the men to land and clearly there were going to be some days each month when this would not be practical. Careful planning was going to be absolutely essential.

'As the floating light's location had to be fixed and she could not move off station, another vessel was going to be needed to carry the men, equipment and supplies to and from the Rock. So, during the spring of 1807 a second ship was prepared for the lighthouse works, one that could serve as a tender and stone lighter.

'They called her the *Smeaton,* after the designer of the Eddystone Light. His notes on the building of that lighthouse had proved to be a valuable source of information in planning this new venture.

'The *Smeaton* was not as large as the floating light, being just over forty tons, but she was specially built so that she would be strong enough to carry all the blocks of stone which would be needed to build the lighthouse tower. They rigged her as a sloop and once again provided living accommodation on board.

'It was planned, in fact, to use this vessel as the main base for the men working on the Rock because she was able to anchor much closer to it than the *Pharos*. However, on those occasions when it was necessary for the *Smeaton* to return to shore for supplies, the men would transfer across to the lightship and continue their work from there. The *Smeaton* did have the great luxury of being able to slip her moorings and head for shelter if conditions at sea became very severe. That was an impossibility for her sister ship, of course, as the *Pharos* had to remain on duty in all weathers.

'Arbroath was the nearest harbour to the Rock and so made the most convenient base for the whole operation. The *Smeaton* arrived there on the 9th August and immediately began to sail backwards and forwards between the Rock and the town. Supplies were needed for those on the floating light and the first equipment required for the operations had to be taken out.

'One of the *Smeaton's* tasks was to lay down several sets of large, mushroom shaped anchors about half a mile away from the Rock itself. Each weighed approximately one and a half tons and floating buoys were attached to them. Any ship coming to the Rock could be fixed to one of these moorings and ride there without having to drop its own anchor.

'Practically speaking, this was very helpful because normal anchors would have hooked onto the rough surface of the rock. They would have been difficult, if not impossible to release. The mushroom shape didn't have this problem. At the end of a season's work it was an easy matter to raise all the anchors and bring them ashore until they were needed again. Their use saved a lot of extra expense.

'Another important aspect which had to be dealt with before the operations began was the hiring of workmen. They were often referred to at the time as artificers and an agreement had to be reached on the wages they were to be paid. Then, as now, the employers and the employees had rather different amounts in mind. After some discussion, the sum of £1.00 per week was agreed upon regardless of whether the men were working on the Rock or at the workyard at Arbroath.

'All who were taken on, however, had to agree to one specific condition - that they would spend one full month at sea before returning ashore. Most of the men involved were either masons, smiths or joiners. They were used to working on land and so there was some concern as to whether or not they would be badly affected by seasickness. The rule applied to everyone (even Robert Stevenson considered himself bound by it) and it was hoped that any initial seasickness would soon disappear as a result.

'Those offshore also had to be fed and the men were

given free rations. These were generous for the period but then the men were going out to do a heavy job in what would often be difficult conditions. Each man received, daily,

750 g (1.5 lb) beef	60 g (2 oz) barley
500 g (1.0 lb) ships biscuit	60 g (2 oz) butter
250 g (8 oz) oatmeal	vegetables
3.5 litres (6 pt) beer	salt.

'Of course at this time the cost of living was very different from today and it was possible to buy five hundred grams of beef for the equivalent of less than three pence. The same quantity of barley was sold for about one pence while whisky was only fifty five pence for four and a half litres!

'In the negotiations, extra premiums were agreed upon to be paid as the work progressed and it was also decided that the men would be paid separately for each tide worked on a Sunday. In effect, double time.

'It was appreciated that the idea of working on a Sunday was a difficult subject. In the early nineteenth century no-one would normally have considered such a thing. They still held firmly to the commandment *"Remember the Sabbath day and keep it holy"*.

'But it was realised in planning the project that to lose one day's work in seven when the working season was limited anyway, could mean that the completion of the lighthouse might be delayed by anything up to a year. That delay might just mean the loss of yet more ships.

'The decision to go ahead with Sunday work was made because the building of the lighthouse was seen as *"an act of humanity"*. In other words, lives would be saved. A farmer, after all, had to attend to his animals on that day and at sea a sailor had to see to his ship. For Robert Stevenson, who had in earlier years considered entering the ministry himself, Sunday work was acceptable in this special case.

'It was appreciated, however, that not everyone might see it that way so the decision as to whether to work or not was left to the individual conscience of each person. Nevertheless, it was made clear to all those who went out to the Rock that if a man did not go there on a Sunday, he would lose his day's wages.

'Regardless of what the men decided to do, it was planned that before any work began on a Sunday morning, everyone would meet on deck for a short service which would include a time of bible reading and prayer.

'By August 1807, all the preparations which it was possible to make had been completed. At last there was nothing to stop them getting out to the Rock and beginning the real work there.'

CHAPTER THREE

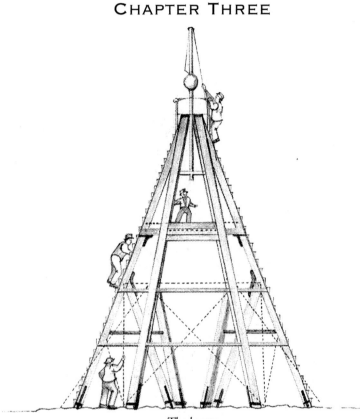

The beacon

THE BEACON

'The first proper workparty to go out to the Rock set sail on Monday, the 17th August 1807. Everything had been carried on board the *Smeaton* by the previous Saturday but the time of sailing was delayed, quite intentionally, because the next day was the Sabbath.

'They left Arbroath at 10 p.m. with the evening tide and it seemed as if a large part of the town's population had come down to the harbour to see them go. The building of the lighthouse had really caught everyone's imagination and many people, young and old, wanted to see the operations begin.

'As the ship moved away from the quayside, there were cheers and waves from those standing nearby. Even the ships moored in the harbour joined in the celebrations. Like the *Smeaton,* they had had their flags flying all day. It was quite a sight.

'There were twenty four men aboard the tender and it was not long before the ship was tied up at her moorings a quarter of a mile away from the Rock. Obviously the hours when the men were able to work there were determined by the time of low tide. Sometimes that could be very early or very late. It certainly did not work out neatly as 9 a.m. to 5 p.m!

'On the Tuesday morning the Rock began to show above the surface of the water at 5 o'clock. Not long afterwards everyone heard the sound of a bell ringing. This was the signal for the men to prepare to leave.

'Soon they were all on deck and climbing down into the three rowing boats which were to take them out to the Rock itself. It was an exciting moment as they moved away from the ship. If any of the men felt just a little bit nervous, it was hardly to be wondered.

'The *Smeaton's* rowing boat could only hold six or eight

people so two boats from the floating light came across to help ferry them ashore. With the total number of men involved there was really only space for two or at most three sailors in each boat.

'One of them would stand at the bow and use a boathook either to push away from the ship or to keep the boat in its channel near the Rock. Another would take the aftmost oar and give the proper time in rowing. But the middle oars had to be rowed by the workmen themselves. Whether they were very proficient in the art beforehand or not, they soon became experts. There was no other way they could get to and from their work at each tide and races between the boats became a favourite amusement.

'The Captain of the *Pharos,* Mr. Sinclair, had been given the job of landing master and so also went with the workparty. It was his responsibility to get everyone and everything required for the operations safely to and from the Rock. He, after all, was the person who had expert knowledge of the sea and the tides.

'Each evening he talked over with Robert Stevenson what the following day's work would entail but it was then the Captain who had to decide when to set out for, or return from, the Rock. While others might offer an opinion, his decision in the matter was final.

'Two landing sites had been chosen as no-one in those early days knew just how much the state of the wind or the tide might affect getting to the Rock. One was on the east side and one on the west. But from the beginning Robert Stevenson made it a rule for himself that he would always be the last man to leave the Rock when they returned to the ship. That way he could be happy in his own mind that everyone was off safely.

'On that first morning the weather was good and they landed without much difficulty. Just as well perhaps! They reached the Rock about 5.30 a.m. but found that the water level had not really gone down far enough to allow work to start. Someone called for three cheers and everyone received a glass of rum. It was a little ceremony that was to be repeated at every important milestone in the building operations.

'By 6 o'clock some of the men were able to begin the task of boring holes into the rock. These were needed to fix the beacon in place. Others began to clear seaweed from the working area and from the paths chosen between it and the landing places. The seaweed was very slippery and there was always a chance that it might cause an accident.

'Not a great deal could be done during that first tide's work. Those who had nothing in particular to do roamed around the Rock, getting to know it. Some picked up coins and other bits and pieces to take back to the ship. Presumably they had come from wrecks.

'One man who did make considerable progress was the blacksmith who came with them, James Dove. He picked a sheltered spot where it was practical for him to set up his forge. The place he chose was near a rock pool so that he would have the water he needed for tempering the iron.

'When everyone landed again in the evening for a second tide's work, all who were able to do so helped the smith set up the fixtures that he needed for his equipment.

'Holes were bored into the surface of the rock and the legs to support the hearth were inserted into them. Wedges of wood and iron were then rammed home to keep the legs secure. A large block of timber was fixed to the rock in the same way and the anvil was placed on it. By 9 p.m. when the men returned to the *Smeaton*, everyone was quite delighted with what they had achieved.

'The work of the smith was very, very important to the whole operation. The sandstone of the rock was very hard and compact. Because of this, any tools that the men used soon became blunt and the smith had to spend a great deal of time resharpening them.

'The larger pieces of his equipment, like the anvil, were left on the Rock between tides. They were so heavy that there was little chance of them being moved or damaged by the sea. This was not the case, however, for the lighter items, including the bellows. They had to be carried backwards and forwards in the rowing boat each time. It is not difficult to imagine how inconvenient this must have been in a small rowing boat packed with people.

'The smith was totally responsible for getting everything he needed to the Rock. This included fuel, the cinders of a former fire, a tinder box and matches. The matches, though, were not the kind which we know today although they were used to carry a flame. The first usable matches to light when they were struck against a rough surface were invented in the 1820's and safety matches did not appear until the middle of the nineteenth century.

'If the smith forgot anything, the work was seriously affected. Once he made the mistake of not bringing his tinder box and it was impossible to get a fire going in the hearth. As he could not sharpen any of the tools, work on the Rock came to a standstill at least an hour before the tide would have forced them to leave.

'On another occasion he fell into the water as he got out of the boat and the tinder was soaked. Once again, no fire meant an early return to the ship.

'At other times it was the sea which brought everything to a stop. Even at low tide the work went on not too far from the water's reach. It was not difficult for a rogue wave to soak the hearth and put out the fire. When that happened, a careful watch always had to be kept so that nothing small or light in weight was washed away.

'However, if conditions permitted, the smith would think nothing of standing knee deep in water to allow the men to continue and therefore get as much done as possible in the time they had available.

'After the smith had his equipment set up to his liking, the main effort went into the preparations for erecting the beacon. Any work on the lighthouse site had to take second place in order to make sure that the Rock was marked before everything came to a standstill over the winter months.

'It took them approximately a month to get the holes for fixing the beacon drilled into the rock. Inevitably it was a fairly slow job. Fifty four holes were needed and they had no power tools at their disposal. Everything was done with simple drills. Now and then the metal bits would snap, but when things went well, they could bore at a rate of about twenty five millimetres per minute.

'At first they were fortunate and were able to land twice a day, making use of the long hours of daylight in summer. With each tide's work, it was sometimes possible to spend over two hours on the Rock and when this happened progress was rapid.

'Then, as the time of low tide moved to later in the day, only one landing was feasible. At the beginning of the operations they did not take a chance in landing when it was dark for reasons of safety. That would change once the Rock was marked because the beacon provided a safe refuge in the event of anything unfortunate happening. Once it was in place the men were able to continue at night by the light of torches.

'When only one landing period was practical each day, the total working time available was automatically cut.

This was also the case as the neap tides approached because the Rock itself was uncovered for a shorter and shorter interval. A further hindrance was encountered when the workparty had to endure their first storm at sea. It did not prove to be a pleasant experience for anyone and brought everything to a standstill for ten days.

'The middle of September had arrived before the drilling work was complete. Only then could the large wooden beams for the beacon be brought out from Arbroath. Further equipment needed to fix the beams in place was also taken out on the *Smeaton* along with extra workmen to help with the job.

'The numbers required on the Rock at any one time always depended on the task in hand. Sometimes, as in this case, more would be brought out from the workyard. On other occasions, if people were no longer needed, they would return ashore.

'The first thing the men had to do was set up a derrick and winch on the rock. That took a whole day in itself but they were needed to lift the heavy beams of the beacon into position.

'Then, because time on the Rock was so precious, everything relating to the operation of setting them in place was meticulously worked out beforehand. Each man knew exactly what his job was. In the situation they were in, it was essential that the work went ahead like clockwork.

'The timber beams that were used were very large.

Each was four hundred and six millimetres square and over fifteen metres in length. But after all the whole idea was that the beacon should be seen above the water level at high tide.

'The only practical way of getting them out to the Rock from the *Smeaton* was to make them into two rafts and float them there. This they were ready to do on the 20th September. At 6 o'clock in the morning a rowing boat took the first raft in tow and it was soon anchored above the building site. Gradually, as the water ebbed, the wood settled slowly onto the rock surface.

'By 7 a.m. work had begun. There were fifty two people on the Rock that day and even the sailors pitched in where they could. In the desperate, yet organised rush to get as much done as possible, the boats landed early in the tide and some of the men began to work waist deep in water.

'Before any of the beams could be lifted into position, two iron bats (or stanchions) had to be fixed to the base of each piece of timber. It was by means of these that the wood would be fixed to the rock surface. The stanchions themselves were a considerable size. Each was one and a half metres long and weighed sixty three and a half kilograms.

'Once they had been fitted around the wood, the beams were raised and the lower parts of the stanchions – about five hundred millimetres – were slipped into the holes which had already been prepared for them. The stanchions were then fixed firmly into place by wedges of fir, oak and iron.

'During that first day's work on the beacon they managed to set up four of the beams and temporarily fix them together at the top. Some of the joiners even stayed behind to complete their work on this after the tide was in. Two of the rowing boats remained behind to take them back to the ship later on. As the other workmen left, it was a great sight to see the first part of the beacon standing clear of the water and their friends working there.

'Fortunately the weather remained fine the next day and it was not a difficult task to lift the other two beams into position. But nothing ever goes perfectly smoothly. Just as the last one was being raised, a hook on the equipment gave way and the beam came crashing down. To everyone's relief no-one was hurt and the wood remained intact. Had it been broken, it would have been a serious matter.

'The upper ends of the beams were mortised together and over the next few weeks the beacon was made as strong as possible. Supporting beams six metres long were added on the inside of each of the main beams. They, too, were fixed to the rock surface by iron stanchions and at the top were bolted to the main structure.

'But long before work on the beacon was anywhere near finished, another storm blew up. Those ships near the Rock, except the floating light of course, had to run for shelter elsewhere. Understandably there was great concern as to how the beacon would cope. It was the first real test of its stability.

'As soon as he was able to do so, Stevenson got back out to the Rock in a rowing boat. Although it was still too rough to land he was very relieved to see that everything appeared to be safe. Nor was he wrong. When the men did eventually return to work, they found that the beacon was intact.

'Once the main beams were in place, the length of a working day was extended for the joiners. It was possible for them to land at either high or low water and work away on anything which had to be done to the beacon above the level of the sea.

'Those who were able to do so stayed there for about eight and a half or nine hours. Any meals they required were cooked on board ship and taken out to them in a rowing boat. But naturally, when the men remained on the Rock, a very careful eye was kept on the state of the weather. No-one wanted to risk having them stranded there.

'Cross beams were fitted and bracing chains were also added to give greater stability. Like the upright beams, the chains were fixed securely to the rock surface at certain points. Over the following winter, however, it was found that the bolts for the chains tended to work free in bad weather. Instead of strengthening the beacon they were more likely to cause damage to it because the loose metalwork was able to bang against the wood. Later on the chains were removed and they were replaced by iron bars.

'As work on the beacon continued they were greatly helped by the fact that it was possible to fix a temporary platform onto the cross beams and James Dove was able to move all his equipment up onto it. Because the platform was above the high water mark he was even able to leave his large bellows there. The fact that he no longer had to carry them backwards and forwards was much appreciated by everyone.

'But fewer masons were now needed at the beacon. Some of them were able to move across to the site of the lighthouse and begin work on preparing the foundation pit.

'The only explosive available at that time was gunpowder. Alfred Nobel did not develop dynamite until 1866. The idea of using explosives to help in the excavation work had been considered but then discarded. It was felt to be too dangerous in that kind of location and there was always the possibility that it might damage the structure of the Rock itself. Instead, they relied upon muscle power and pickaxes. The smith was permanently kept busy sharpening the points of the tools.

'They continued on the excavation work right up until October. By then the daylight hours were much shorter and they often had to rely on torchlight for an evening tide. It was also inevitable that poor weather and sea conditions became more and more of a problem as the year advanced. Work could not really carry on for much longer.

'The men therefore set about the task of completing the last few jobs to be done. To protect the wood, the upper part of the beacon was painted white. The lower part of the structure (up to the point the spring tides would reach) was charred and covered with several coats of boiling pitch. And at the very top they fitted a small flagstaff and flag.

'When finished, the beacon could be clearly seen at high water. The top stood almost fourteen metres above the Rock surface. On two of the beams footholds had been fitted which allowed the men to climb up easily. Now, were a shipwreck to occur, they could be used by any survivors stranded there.

'Once on the beacon, they would have a refuge until rescue was possible. With the *Pharos* only a couple of miles away, that would not be difficult. And, just in case this happened, a tin chest containing ship's biscuits and several bottles of fresh water was left behind.

'Before the final jobs had been completed John Rennie arrived to see, in person, how things were progressing. He was on his way north to Fraserburgh because he was also advising on harbour works there. It was obvious to him, too, how well the work had gone.

'Everyone then returned ashore in the *Smeaton*

along with all the equipment they had used. Nothing more in the way of building work could be done on the Rock until the next spring.

'Over the winter Francis Watt, the foreman wright, was left with the task of checking the beacon periodically as he was the man responsible for that part of the operations. His instructions were to take three or four workmen with him, if the weather was reasonable at the time of the spring tides, and make any necessary repairs to ensure that the beacon remained safe.'

CHAPTER FOUR

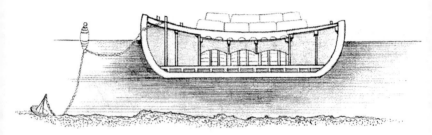

A section of a praam boat and a mushroom anchor

WIND, WEATHER AND DANGER

'The main achievement of that first season's work was undoubtedly the marking of the Rock by the lightship and the beacon. But a great deal of important experience had also been gained.

'Everyone was now much more confident about the practicalities of working offshore and in getting the men and supplies out to the Rock. They had also learned just how important an element the weather was going to be while they were working there.

'Their first experience of how quickly conditions could change had come only a couple of days after the whole operation began. The morning shift had ended and the men had begun to row back to the *Smeaton*. Before they reached her they were suddenly enveloped in fog. They could not see a thing in front of them and had no idea where the ship lay.

'As it happened it was only a mist drifting in from the sea (what we, hereabouts, call a haar) but in order to guide the boats back to safety, the crew of the *Smeaton* had to blow on a horn and occasionally fire a musket. Those who were steering were able to do so by sound, if not by sight. Fortunately, by evening it was once again clear and there was no problem in rowing back to the Rock.

'Something very similar happened during another season's work but with rather different results. A number of sailors were rowing, in fog, between two of the ships anchored near the Rock and completely missed the one they were heading for. By the time they realised what had happened they had no option but to keep going and eventually landed in Fife! Next morning the weather was clear and they rowed all the way back. Understandably, when the men finally climbed on board they were exhausted.

'The first spell of rough weather which the work party faced during that first season happened to coincide with a time when everyone had moved across to the *Pharos* because the *Smeaton* had returned to Arbroath for supplies.

'With the lightship anchored so much further from the Rock, they found it far more difficult and tiring to row the extra distance between the two. It was not easy to cope with the heavy seas and the strong wind in the open rowing boats. In fact the men were frequently drenched by spray from the waves before they even got to work. They must have felt very uncomfortable beginning a new shift when they were cold and damp.

'When the men were stationed on the *Pharos* it sometimes took them as long as two hours to row back to the ship after their spell of work at the building site. Occasionally an oar was lost on the way and, if a wave came over a boat, a couple of those on board had to bail furiously so that it didn't sink. When they did get back to their quarters after a difficult journey what everyone needed (and got) was an extra dram, a change of clothing and a good hot meal.

'Of course if the state of the weather deteriorated too far at any time, there was no alternative but to suspend work until it improved. This could mean that everything was at a standstill for several days on end and the men were totally confined to whichever ship they happened to be on. It usually meant a pretty rough ride either way.

'The *Smeaton* always tried to stay at anchor near the Rock for as long as possible in bad weather but it was sometimes necessary for her to run for the shelter of Arbroath harbour or St. Andrew's Bay. Once the storm in question had run its course, she would return to her station. For those on the *Pharos,* however, there was never any option but to sit it out.

'Conditions on the floating light when the men were stationed there were, in fact, not so cramped as those on the *Smeaton* because the *Pharos* was a far larger vessel. The crew's quarters on the lightship were at the front of the ship while the workmen had their berths near the middle. There was the galley, of course, where the food was prepared and next to it was a large cabin used by the Captain, the Mate and the Principal Lightkeeper. The foremen shared it when they, too, were on board while Robert Stevenson had a small room for his own use at the rear of the vessel.

'However the men did not like living on the *Pharos* at all. They preferred the more confined accommodation of the *Smeaton*. It was not just the extra rowing involved but the fact that the lightship rolled badly in heavy seas. Her shape may have been ideal for the job she had to do but the constant pitching meant that everyone suffered dreadfully from seasickness when on board. For most of the workers, that problem had soon been conquered on the *Smeaton*.

'The worst storm of all during that first season took place at the beginning of September and, as luck would have it, Stevenson and his men were again on the *Pharos* when it broke. A fierce gale blew up and the swell of the sea became so great that the crew had to run out more of the ship's cable. Every wave which struck the vessel caused her to shake and one wave fell so heavily on the skylight of Stevenson's cabin that the glass was broken.

'Although the Captain and crew of the lightship had every confidence in her ability to ride out the storm, the workmen stationed on her were not so sure. As she pitched and rolled in the rough seas there were several occasions when they thought she was about to sink. Water sometimes poured down into the living quarters and everything there was pretty damp and cheerless. The men were tossed about so much that they even found it difficult to stay in bed!

'Despite the dreadful conditions, there was always a sailor on watch. Each took his turn and for two hours would lash himself to one of the masts with a piece of rope so that he could not be washed overboard. The only clothes he wore were a jacket and trousers because a coat would have meant more to dry off later on. There were no waterproofs available in those days. On his head he wore a hat, held in place by one of the old fashioned napkins which sailors used to wear. It was tied underneath his chin.

'Apparently the artist J.M.W. Turner did exactly the same thing before he started to paint a picture of a storm at sea. In order to be able to depict the conditions accurately, he knew he would first of all have to experience them for himself. He told the ship's crew that they were not to release him regardless of how much he might beg them to do so. The painting which Turner produced afterwards was a masterpiece and interestingly, he also drew a picture of the completed Bell Rock lighthouse in a storm.

'For those on the *Pharos* on that particular occasion, it was twenty four hours before the storm began to ease. With everyone confined below and feeling pretty miserable, the first sound of the crew's footsteps on the deck above made them wonder if the worst was about to happen. But they were soon reassured that all was well and that conditions were beginning to improve.

'The cook set about lighting the galley fire and preparing a hot meal for everyone – their first for some time. It was very, very welcome. Gradually things began to return to normal and it was possible to get everything dried off. It is hardly surprising that after a spell of weather of this kind, the men were always desperately keen to get back to their work on dry land at the Rock.

'It became more and more clear, however, as that first season continued that the original plan to use the *Pharos* as an extra base for the men was just not going to work. She was too far away from the Rock for convenience and, practically speaking, another solution had to be found.

'The problem was laid before the Commissioners and they agreed to the building of a new tender which would be ready for the next season's work. It could be permanently anchored near the Rock leaving the *Smeaton* free to sail wherever she was needed.

'In the short term, the Lighthouse Board's yacht was made available instead. She was used each year for a tour of inspection during which all the lighthouses around the

Scottish coast were visited. It was agreed that once this had been done, the yacht would come to the Rock and act as a second tender. As a result, the long rows to work and seasickness became a thing of the past.

'When the *Smeaton* did have to go back to Arbroath for supplies, everyone at sea looked forward to her return. The men spent a long time away from their families and friends but they knew that the *Smeaton* would bring with her newspapers, letters, clean clothes and other items from home.

'As their working hours were so limited, the men inevitably had to spend long periods of the day on board ship while the water level on the Rock was too high to land. There must have been times when this weighed heavily on them but they became adept at keeping themselves occupied. They would read, fish, tell stories or even dry off clothes when that was necessary. There were always some people around who could play musical instruments and it was not difficult to organise entertainments to help pass the hours.

'Letters from home were eagerly awaited. Most of the men wrote regularly to their families on shore and all their correspondence went post free. This was an important perk because before the introduction of the penny post in 1840, postal charges were quite expensive. Around 1800 it cost more than five pence to send a single sheet letter from London to Edinburgh. That was over twelve times the cost forty years later. It is not surprising, therefore, that many letters of the period show writing crossed and recrossed. By doing this the sender was able to write as much as possible without having to go to the expense of mailing a second sheet.

'Unfortunately during that first season the danger of working so far from land was brought home only too well when the workparty on the Rock came very close to drowning. The incident took place on the 2nd September, before drilling at the site of the beacon had been completed and while the men were still engaged on the preparatory work. As a result, the beams for the beacon had not yet been been brought out to the Rock and the workparty remained totally dependent on the rowing boats for their safety once the tide began to rise.

'There was nothing unusual at first and the men landed as they normally did for a tide's work. Most of them had rowed from the *Pharos* but the *Smeaton's* boat arrived with an extra eight men who had been brought from Arbroath on her last trip and for whom there was no room on the lightship. The wind was quite strong and the sea a bit rough but not so bad that it was impossible to land. Once all the workmen were there, the boat from the *Smeaton* returned to the ship so that the sailors could check the ropes used to fix her to the buoy of the floating anchor.

'Unfortunately, not long after they reached her, the ship broke free and of course she carried the rowing boat with her. Before anyone realised what had happened the *Smeaton* had drifted quite a distance away from her moorings.

'The ship was not in any danger herself, but those on the Rock were. Without the *Smeaton's* boat they could not get everyone off safely. Once those on the *Smeaton* realised what had happened, the crew worked feverishly to raise the mainsail in order to try and return to her moorings but they had the wind and tide against them. Her master, Captain Pool, was desperately worried and did not know what to do for the best. It was perfectly clear that he could not get back to the Rock before it was covered with water.

'On the Rock itself, it was only Robert Stevenson and the landing master who were at first aware of what had happened and how serious the situation was. There were thirty two men on the Rock and only two boats left. Even in good weather they could have carried no more than twenty four people but the conditions were becoming rougher all the time and as a result only eight per boat could be chanced. If there was a rush for the limited places available, neither man was sure just what might happen.

'The tide turned and the water slowly began to rise. It was almost inevitable, with the way the sea was running, that the forge would be extinguished earlier than usual that day. The men started to clear everything and to think about returning to the boats. One by one, they realised what had happened and not a word was spoken. They just stood there, each taking stock of the situation they found themselves in. A dreadful silence descended on the Rock.

'Stevenson and the landing master continued to think desperately of ways in which they might be able to get everyone off safely but with the *Smeaton* adrift, it was a long way to the floating light. There was not enough time to send some back to her and then return to the Rock for the rest before it was covered with water. And no-one stood a chance in the rough seas if they tried to leave with the extra men clinging to the boats. When Stevenson tried to speak to the men he found his mouth was so dry that he could not utter a word.

'Then, just as things looked very, very black, someone caught sight of another vessel coming towards them.

'It turned out to be James Spink, the Bell Rock pilot, bringing letters from Arbroath. At first he did not realise that there was anything wrong and, with the weather as it was, had not in fact expected to find anyone working there. But he soon took in the situation and came as close to the Rock as he was able. It was a simple matter, then, to ferry sixteen of the men to his boat with instructions to go on to the *Pharos*.

'The remaining sixteen followed in the two rowing boats and despite the fact that it was a very difficult journey back taking three hours to cover about a mile, everyone was more than relieved to be off the Rock. By the time they reached the ship, the men in the rowing boats were utterly exhausted but at least they were safe.

Robert Stevenson readily admitted in later years that for as long as he lived he would never be able to forget the experience of standing on the Rock that day.

'There was no doubt at all that in arriving when he did, James Spink saved many lives. Later on, in recognition of this, the Lighthouse Board gave him a small pension. James Spink lived until he was ninety five and Robert Stevenson visited him while on a trip to Arbroath in 1832.

'Several things were highlighted by this near disaster. Firstly, the fact was reinforced that another ship was needed to act as a tender but it was also clear that safety procedures had to be reviewed. This was immediately done; safer mooring methods were decided upon and the rule was made that no boat left the Rock without its full complement of men.

'Most of all, the incident showed how important the beacon would be. Had it (or even part of it) been in place at the time of the accident there would at least have been something for the men to hold on to until help arrived. By the end of the 1807 season the beacon was, of course, in position and they then felt much more confident about their own safety while they were at work.

'It was not really surprising that when the bell rang the next morning telling everyone to prepare to return to the Rock, eighteen of the men refused to go. It was the only time anyone had done this except for four masons who had, from the beginning, said they would not work on a

Sunday. That problem had not proved to be as difficult as everyone imagined it might be.

'However, the first four men into the boat that morning were those very masons. Stevenson, the foreman, and some others joined them and as the weather was now fine, they managed to get four hours work done.

'By evening the rest had had a chance to get over their fears and they, too, went back to the Rock. Everything returned to a more normal routine. Nevertheless, it must have been quite a thought for them all to return to the spot where they had so nearly drowned the day before. And, as it happened, from then onwards the four masons also decided to work on a Sunday.

'Even at this early stage in the operations, one important question remained at the back of everyone's minds as far as the weather and the state of the sea were concerned. How easy or difficult would it be to land the heavy stone blocks which were needed to build the lighthouse tower?

'After all, regardless of what the conditions were like, large numbers of blocks would have to be brought out and they would have to be landed safely. If one was broken or even damaged, the whole operation might grind to a halt until a new stone could be cut to the correct size.

'In order to discover any likely problems, they carried out an experiment. The *Smeaton* brought out from Arbroath six large blocks of granite and a praam boat. This was a boat about nine metres long but it was made in such a way as to be especially buoyant. Its shape, although much smaller, was not unlike that of the *Pharos* and for the same reasons.

'The praam had been designed in such a way as to be able to carry, in smooth weather, as much as six or seven tons on deck. Its name actually came about by accident after someone mentioned that the boat's shape reminded them of a certain type of Norwegian craft. As can so often happen, the word stuck.

'The plan was that when building work actually began, the *Smeaton* would bring the blocks of cut stone out from Arbroath. They would then be transferred to a praam boat and it could be towed to moorings close to the Rock. The praam would remain there until the stones were needed on site. The question was would it actually work? Could the heavy stones be landed without too much difficulty or without any of the workmen being hurt in the process? Hopefully, the experiment would highlight any likely problems.

'The granite blocks were loaded onto the praam and because the occasion was rather special, the praam was decorated with flags. At low tide she was pulled by two rowing boats to the eastern creek and there Stevenson went on board to check everything. A lot depended on this operation.

'It was not possible for the praam to float right up the creek as far as the building site so her cargo was delivered onto the part of the Rock they called *Smith's Ledge*. From there the stones were pushed along on planks of wood. To everyone's delight (and probably relief as well) it all worked perfectly. The whole exercise went much more smoothly than anyone had ever expected.

'With this success there was nothing more for the praam to do at present so it was taken back to Arbroath. The blocks themselves were not needed for anything and were left on the Rock. They were not even removed when work ended for the season and spent the winter there. By the next spring the force of the sea had scattered them in all directions.

'The fact that the experiment had worked was very important. They knew that they could move forward, confidently, to the next phase of the operation. Everything was beginning to look very promising for the following year when the real blocks of stone for the lighthouse would arrive.'

CHAPTER FIVE

A course of patterns by which the stones were cut

THE WORKYARD

'One thing, of course, which was essential for a building operation of this nature was a base ashore.

'Nothing except a few pieces of heavy equipment could be left on the Rock itself and only a limited amount of material could be kept on the ships anchored nearby. A workyard (where everything could be prepared and stored until required offshore) was absolutely vital. Without this facility, the construction work would not have gone ahead so smoothly.

'Earlier on, before much of the other work had begun a number of possible sites for the yard had been looked at in Arbroath. In the end a seven year lease was taken out on an area of ground down on Ladyloan. The rent asked for was £21 per year, quite a large amount for the time and serious consideration had to be given to this fact because every effort had to be made to keep costs to a minimum. However, as the location could not be bettered, the terms were finally accepted.

'It meant that the yard was less than three hundred metres away from the harbour, an important factor when thinking of all the stones and materials which had to be brought to it and then taken back out to the Rock.

'Two men were put in charge there. One was David Logan who, as clerk of works, was responsible for the hewing department (in other words the cutting of the stones). The other was Lachlan Kennedy, the engineer's clerk. He saw to all the accounts and paperwork.

'The yard itself was over three thousand square metres in size but in addition they required a whole range of offices, workshops, stores and even stabling facilities. Accommodation had to be built for the men working at the yard and this was referred to as the artificer's barrack. All these buildings took up one whole side of the workyard and they had to be in place before much else could be done.

'Along the other three sides wooden shelters were constructed so that the men could work under cover in wet weather. Another item which had to be built was a kiln, needed in the preparation of lime for the lighthouse mortar. Nothing came pre-packed then.

'At the very centre of the yard they also made a circular platform of stone. It was almost thirteen and a half metres in diameter and so was wider than the base of the lighthouse would be once it was completed. As a result, the stones for a particular course (or layer) of the tower could be placed on it to ensure that they fitted correctly. It was important that no adjustment was necessary to the blocks once they had been taken out to the Rock and, after checking, the stones were set aside until they were required.

'The platform was obviously going to have to support a considerable weight so it needed a substantial foundation. What they did was rather like the old process used in building roads. They dug out a pit about three quarters of a metre deep and, after putting a layer of large stones at the base, filled in much of the rest with rubble.

'Then, to complete everything, a layer of dressed sandstone blocks was set on top. They came from the quarries which were then in existence at the cliffs to the north of Arbroath. Once these stones were in place, the top of the platform was level with the surface of the ground.

'The tower of the lighthouse, apart from supporting the lighting apparatus, had to do two things. It had to be strong enough to withstand the sea (otherwise the light itself would be in danger) and it also had to provide living accommodation for the keepers who would man it. They were, after all, a long way from shore.

'To give the structure strength, it was planned to build the lighthouse with a solid base of stone blocks nine metres in height. Furthermore, the concave shape of the lower part of the tower was designed to help reduce the force of the sea on the masonry. Above that level the structure was to be hollow and there would be space within the walls for rooms in which the men could live.

'At first it was hoped to use sandstone for the inner stonework and granite for the whole of the outer casing. As granite is so resistant to erosion by the sea, this would have made the whole structure very strong indeed.

'Sandstone blocks were ordered from the Mylnefield quarries near Dundee and granite ones from Rubislaw at Aberdeen. But as it turned out, it was very difficult to get enough granite blocks of the correct size. Eventually stone agents had to be sent around all the granite quarries of Aberdeenshire in an attempt to obtain the necessary quantities. This scarcity of suitable stone meant that the cost of the blocks rose to three, and in some cases four times the original price quoted. The final cost of the lighthouse was increased as a result.

'The sandstone blocks did not prove to be so much of a problem but the supply did tend to dry up over the winter months. In frosty weather the stone had a tendency to split and so it was not practical to continue quarrying then. The masons employed by the quarry were laid off work until conditions improved.

'In the end, granite was only used to case the lower, solid part of the lighthouse. That, however, was the part which would bear the full force of the sea. The upper part of the lighthouse was built of sandstone, like the core of the base. But ensuring that the masons at the yard had a steady supply of blocks to work on proved to be a major headache for many, many months.

'In his design for the Eddystone Light, John Smeaton was the first person to try using a system of interlocking stones in each course. This gave a far, far greater strength to the building than ordinary blocks and so the same idea was used here. The only slight difference at the Bell Rock was that the stones were longer in shape towards the centre of the building and less wide on the outside. It was hoped that this would give an even greater strength.

'The blocks fitted together very much like the pieces of a jigsaw. It is difficult, if not impossible to pull the pieces of a jigsaw apart. The only way to separate them is to lift one piece up and away from the others.

'In just the same way, by using shaped blocks for the lighthouse, one stone could not be washed out leaving the whole structure weakened. A block could only be removed by lifting it vertically and so once a further layer had been placed on top, there was no likelihood of any real damage being done.

'This idea, however, meant that the blocks of stone had to be cut very accurately indeed and different shapes of stone were also needed. To help the masons do this, moulds or patterns were prepared for the stones and each course required several moulds.

'The moulds themselves were made out of strips of fir wood and they were then strengthened with thin plates of iron. It was important that no damage was done to any of these as the slightest variation in the dimensions might mean a cut stone would not fit into place.

'After each stone had been cut to shape and checked, it was marked so that those on the Rock knew exactly where it fitted. But even when all the stones for a course had been completed, the moulds for it were carefully put aside until that course had been laid in place on the Rock. By doing this, had there been an accident and something happened to one of the stones, it would not have been a difficult matter to immediately cut another block to shape.

'No-one expected any of the stones to weigh more than two tons in their finished state but when they came straight from the quarries they were much heavier. Because of the dovetailing (as the interlocking system was called), there was a great deal of waste produced in cutting them to size.

'The size of blocks available at the yard determined which stones could be cut. As a result it was often impossible for the masons to work methodically on one course before going on to the next. Instead, at any one time they were frequently involved in cutting stones for a variety of layers.

'The fact that the two kinds of rock were very different in character was also important. It meant that two squads of masons were needed, one made up of men who were experienced in cutting granite and the other of those who were used to working with sandstone.

'The problem of moving the heavy blocks around the yard (perhaps several times for each one) was made easier by the use of a carpenter's jack. This was a tool used in the shipyards of the period to lift the vessels up onto blocks for repair. All ships were made of wood then, and not of iron. The jack was just as helpful at the Bell Rock workyard because it allowed a man to move even the heaviest of stones by himself.

'All the stone blocks, of course, had to be brought from the quarries to Arbroath harbour by sea. Poor road conditions made this the fastest and most economical way of doing it. They were carried to the yard from the quay by a special type of cart called a Woolwich sling cart.

'It was a type which had long been used by military engineers. Instead of a stone being lifted up onto the body of the carriage it was suspended instead between the two wheels. This was done by means of a system of gears fixed to the frame of the cart.

'The chain on the cart used to lift each stone was attached to the blocks by means of lewis bats. Each lewis was made of several pieces of iron, part of which was inserted into a hole specially cut for it in the stone. Some of the larger blocks required two lewis' to get a proper balance and they were also needed on the Rock for laying the stones in place.

'The task of carrying all the stones to the yard from the harbour and then, in due course, back again for shipment out to the Rock fell to James Craw and his horse Bassey. The two of them became quite famous in their own way and afterwards Bassey went to live in well earned retirement on Inchkeith Island in the Firth of Forth. The horse eventually died there in 1813.

'Over the winter of 1807/8, the *Smeaton* sailed backwards and forwards bringing stones to the yard while the lighthouse yacht served as a tender for the floating light. Depending on the quantity of stone available, forty to sixty men worked on cutting the blocks to shape but by spring everything was well behind schedule.

'Although the stones of the lighthouse were to be fixed permanently by mortar, until it had set the force of the sea was potentially strong enough to move blocks out of position. This danger would exist until the building was above the reach of the tide.

'Something was needed to help keep the stones in place and the answer lay in joggles, wedges and trenails. Large quantities of these items were brought in to the workyard to be stored until they were required at the Rock.

'Joggles were square or cubical stones which were sunk, every so often, half into a lower course and half into the course above. By linking two stones together in that way the joggles made it difficult for the weight of water in any wave to move part of the structure horizontally. In other words it prevented the stonework being shifted sideways, out of alignment.

'The wedges, on the other hand, were made of wood and were almost half a metre long. They were pushed down into the perpendicular (or upright) joints to make sure that the dovetails of the stones fitted perfectly.

'While the joggles and wedges helped keep the horizontal and vertical joints in position, the trenails prevented any stone being lost because of the sea forcing it up and out of place. The trenails were long narrow rods of oak six hundred and ten millimetres long and thirty two millimetres in diameter. Two were inserted into every stone block which was laid in order to fix it permanently to the other immediately underneath.

'To do this, a hole bored all the way through the top stone was continued one hundred and fifty two millimetres into the one below. The wooden trenail was then forced home, linking the two. Each trenail was itself made firm by the use of small wedges and even if the mortar was washed away, the trenails were able to hold the blocks together until the upper stone could be relayed.

'Although the main strength of the lighthouse would eventually come from the weight of the stone structure, great care was also taken over the quality of the mortar used to set the stones in place.

'Centuries before, the Romans had known about cement. They realised that if certain proportions of lime and clay were mixed together with water, a very hard substance resulted. For their building works, they mixed lime with volcanic earth and other forms of burnt clay in the proportions of one part lime to two parts of clay. The fact that so many of their bridges, aqueducts and other masonry still exist testifies to its strength. But this knowledge was lost in the Dark Ages after the fall of the Roman Empire.

'It was only when John Smeaton was carrying out experiments for the Eddystone lighthouse that a real understanding of the importance of the lime/clay mix was regained. He used a mixture of lime from Aberthaw in Wales and pozzolano (or pozzolana) from Italy, an earthy lava which the Romans themselves had used. Fifty years after the Eddystone light had been built, Smeaton's mortar was still considered to be the best available for this purpose.

'As far as the Bell Rock lighthouse was concerned, lime

could still be obtained from Aberthaw but with Napoleon's armies in control of Italy, it was impossible to get any supplies of pozzolano. Instead, they managed to track down a quantity of tarras (trass) from Holland. Its composition was very similar to the other and it was used by the Dutch in the building of dykes.

'The other two constituents of the mortar – sand and water – could be obtained locally. Sand was taken from the coast half a mile to the south of Arbroath and there was no shortage of water out on the Rock itself! Although it might have been preferable to use fresh water rather than salt, there was no way that the quantities they required could be taken out by boat. Sea water had been used in the building of the Eddystone light and no ill effects had been found. It would have to be used here too.

'Although very strong once it had set, this type of mortar took a long time to become firm. As a result there was every possibility that at least some of it might be washed away by the sea. To try and prevent this, a new type of cement was tried which hardened almost immediately. It was much too expensive to use in large quantities but at least it could be used for pointing the exterior joints and so protect the main mortar.

'Preparations for other aspects of the next season's work also went ahead. True to their word, the Commissioners authorized the purchase of an eighty one ton vessel already on the stocks at Arbroath to serve as the new tender.

'She was named *Sir Joseph Banks* after the famous

naturalist. He had been one of those who had leant their weight to the proposals which went before Parliament and this was a way of showing everyone's appreciation of the contribution he had made. The vessel's interior layout was very similar to that of the Pharos and they rigged her as a schooner. This meant that she could be got under sail quickly, if that was necessary, and it was also possible to stow two large boats on deck.

'In planning the two boats for the *Sir Joseph Banks,* the experience and memories of the year before were not forgotten. They were made as large as possible - six metres long - and were able to carry nineteen men each. The names given to the boats were the *Mason* and the *Seaman.* However, because of the near disaster they had all faced they borrowed some ideas from Henry Greatheart's early lifeboats. One of the tender's boats was lined with cork so that it could act in such a capacity if necessary and it was able to float with thirty on board.

'Three new praam boats were built and they, too, were designed to double as lifeboats. They were made watertight and twelve empty casks were stowed in each hold to ensure that they remained buoyant.

'Equipment had also to be ordered for the next stage of the operations on the Rock. Wooden pumps, for example, were going to be needed to clear the foundation pit of the water left in it after each tide had receded. As the excavations went deeper, that would become a bigger and bigger task.

'Then, in order to move the heavy blocks for the lighthouse, a number of different cranes and winches were required. Being made of iron they could be left on the Rock between tides as they would not be easily moved. They were needed at the landing stages to lift the stones from the praams and on the building site itself when laying the blocks carefully into position.

'Another matter which had to be dealt with was the transporting of the blocks from the landing stages to where the construction work was going ahead. They could not risk any stones being damaged at this point and the only practical solution lay in the use of railway tracks.

'Two of these were to be built, one from each of the landing places. However, because of all the irregularities on the rock surface, the tracks had to be specially designed and built for this particular purpose. Like much of the other equipment, the railways were made of cast iron and were ordered from Shotts Iron Works.

'The track itself was about three quarters of a metre wide but it had to be supported on special iron frames in order to overcome any variations in surface level. The frames were fixed to the rock underneath and were anything from a hundred and fifty two millimetres to one and a half metres in height. The end result was a system of railway lines raised above all the uneven rock.

'The little wagons for the railway (on which a block

would rest) were also made almost entirely of iron. Anything else might have been washed away by the sea and they, too, would have to remain behind between the tides. They were quite simple in design with four wheels three hundred and fifty six millimetres in diameter. The only wooden part was some timber bolted on top to form a seat for the stones. At either end there was a place to fix a detachable handle and this enabled the men, who had to pull the wagons themselves, to move them in either direction.

'By the end of March 1808, Robert Stevenson had left his home in Edinburgh and was back in Arbroath. With this vast amount of preparatory work more or less complete, he wanted to check everything. The start of another season's work was very much on his mind.'

CHAPTER SIX

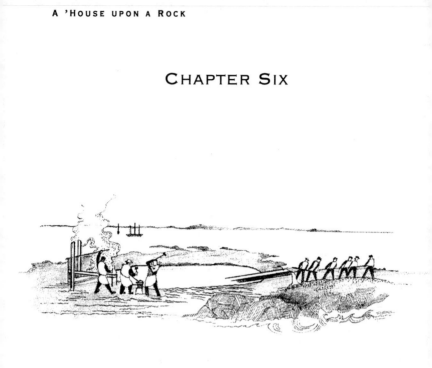

The smiths, the foundation pit and a wooden pump in use

1808: THE FOUNDATION PIT, PROBLEMS AND PRESS-GANGS

'In the spring, when he got back out to the Rock for a preliminary visit, Robert Stevenson was delighted to find the beacon in excellent condition. It was still absolutely solid and the rough seas of the winter had made no real impact on it.

'The only slight difference was in its colour. The lower part was now green due to a covering of algae while the top offered plenty of evidence to suggest that it had been much appreciated by passing seabirds! No ship had come to grief on the Rock during the winter months so, fortunately, the beacon and the floating light had served their purpose.

'The chest of provisions which had been left behind was found intact. When they looked inside, the ship's biscuits (which had been stored in a tin canister) were still in good condition.

'However six of the eighteen glass bottles containing water had shattered. This was put down at the time, rightly or wrongly, to the water inside them freezing. Another possible cause – the shaking of the beacon – was dismissed as unlikely because any movement in the structure was very small.

'The first proper workparty of 1808 left Arbroath on the 25th May. They were able to set out more confidently for this second season's work than they had done the year before and along with Stevenson there was Peter Logan, twelve masons, two smiths and thirteen seamen. Included in the latter were the master and mate of the new tender, the *Sir Joseph Banks,* and also a steward to attend to the men's needs.

'In the intervening months James Wilson had taken over from Mr. Sinclair as Captain of the *Pharos.* He was to remain in that post and so act as landing master until the lighthouse was finished. On the 26th May he led his first party out to the Rock and they got there at eight in the morning. The lighthouse flag was immediately hoisted to the top of the beacon to show that work was once more in progress.

'A temporary platform was again fixed to the cross beams of the beacon and the smith and his assistant set about the job of getting the forge into operation. The platform which they had used the previous year had been taken away in order to limit the destructive effect of the waves on the beacon during the winter.

'As far as the masons were concerned, they had to get back to the work of excavating the foundation pit. It needed to be, on average, three hundred and fifty six millimetres deep so they had quite a task in front of them. Some parts of the site were higher than others so while considerable areas had to be levelled off, in other instances holes had to be filled in. Once the pit was finished it would be possible for the first courses of the lighthouse to be secured firmly to the rock surface.

'The sailors with the party also kept themselves busy. They cleared the seaweed and shellfish which had once again gathered over the winter months and made themselves useful wherever they could. They helped the masons, for example, by carrying tools which needed to be resharpened to the smith and that was an enormous help as it saved the masons a great deal of valuable time.

'The sailors also took away any chippings of rock which accumulated in the foundation pit because they tended to become quite a nuisance to the men as they worked there. The chippings were carried out to the *Smeaton* in boats and she then used them as ballast on her return journeys.

'By this time there were about thirty five seamen employed in the lighthouse service. But they were all in danger of being lost when orders were given for the establishment of an *impress* at Arbroath. This was a means of making it legal for officers from the navy to force people to serve on their ships. As few men were prepared to willingly man naval vessels in the war with Napoleon, the impress had already been in force at other, larger, ports.

'Conditions in the navy then were very different from today and there were never enough volunteers to be found. The press gangs (as they were called) would go round ports looking for likely victims. Merchant seamen and fishermen were very much at risk because they were already used to conditions at sea. But landsmen would be taken if the gangs were desperate and sometimes the impress system was even used as a convenient way of clearing out prisons.

'It was obvious that if many of the seamen serving on the lighthouse ships were lost, the whole building operation might be affected. The only thing to be done was to approach the Admiralty and ask for protection to be granted to the Lighthouse Board's sailors. The men would then be free to go about their duties and return ashore without fear of being press-ganged.

'Fortunately, this request was granted and an exemption was given. Each ship received a certificate of protection on which the details of every seaman had to be carefully recorded. However the individual sailors could not carry this around with them. Instead, each man was given a ticket with a description of himself on it. It was attached to a silver medal bearing the Lighthouse Board's name and motto. As long as they carried them, the men were able to prove their identity if they were challenged at any time.

'Serving on the lighthouse ships became more popular with seamen as a result. During the previous year it had not always been easy to obtain the full complement of men needed for each vessel because, especially in the case of the floating light, they had to spend several weeks at a time on board. Now and again there had been complaints from some of the sailors if their leave was delayed by bad weather.

'It was a very different matter once this official protection was given. From then on, manning the ships was not usually a problem. And, as it happened, the impress system (which was considered by the vast majority of people to be most unfair) was never again used after 1815 when the Napoleonic Wars came to an end.

'With that problem solved, everyone's attention returned to matters on the Rock. While work continued on the foundation pit, the *Smeaton* brought out a quantity of cast iron rails and Norwegian logs so that the building of the railways could begin. It was important that work on these went ahead as quickly as possible because hopefully the first stones for the lighthouse would begin to arrive in a few week's time.

'In the meantime, the cast iron pieces were laid carefully into crevices in the rock surface. This was to protect them and prevent them being moved about by the sea until they were required. The logs were needed to support the railways across gullies or similar features and like the metalwork they, too, had to be fixed firmly to the rock.

'Once again, when the water level rose and the first tide's work came to an end, the smith and one or two others did not return to the tender. They chose instead, as they had done the year before, to remain on the beacon. It was a good opportunity to sharpen tools or make any extra fixtures which were needed for the tracks. That way everything was ready for the men on their return.

'The subject of Sunday work resurfaced when a delegation from the men asked if they could have a word with Robert Stevenson. This was something of a surprise as the matter had posed no particular problem the year before. But the men came with a request that they be paid only for an ordinary seven day's work. They did not want to receive the extra payment made for a second tide's landing on a Sunday as had been done the year before.

'In asking for this, the men felt that they would be making the point quite clear, especially to those who were critical of their actions, that they were only working on a Sunday to ensure that the lighthouse was built as quickly as possible. They were not doing it for the extra money involved.

'Robert Stevenson understood the reasons behind their request and so granted it. In fact when speaking of the building operations in later years he always insisted that it was impossible to speak highly enough of the commitment and effort given by all the men involved.

'While digging continued at the foundation pit and the construction of the railways began, the joiners who now came out to the Rock began a different task altogether.

'The idea of constructing a wooden cabin on the beacon had been considered early on but that possibility had depended totally on how stable the beacon proved to be. Having such a facility would be a great help as it could fulfil a number of roles. It could be a refuge should there be an accident and a place to cook meals instead of having to bring them out from one of the ships. It could also act as a base where at least some of the men would be able to live during the working months without having to return to the tender.

'Those who had remained on the beacon at high tide the year before had been perfectly confident of their safety and had welcomed not having to row back so often to the ships. For any workmen who were affected by seasickness, staying there had come as a welcome relief. Now, the fact that the beacon had withstood the winter gales so well made the idea of building a cabin on it quite practical.

'The first thing they did was fit up a second platform. The joists for it were fixed securely to the main beams but the flooring was only lightly nailed so that it would lift easily in a heavy sea without damaging the whole structure. It was planned in any case to remove the boards of this floor at the end of each season and leave only the joists in place.

'Once it had been completed, the new platform stood over seven and a half metres above the Rock and another smith was able to work there. As it was also the place where all the mortar for the lighthouse would be mixed in due course, the platform was given the name *the mortar gallery*. But it had no walls. It was left open to the fresh air and that probably made it a lot safer and more pleasant for those working in the confined space available.

'Immediately above the platform, a wooden cabin was built around the top of the beacon. It was quite a large task to undertake and it was not made easier by the fact that all the timber and materials required had to be brought out in the small boats.

'Although the space inside was not large, there were three different floor levels. It was planned to use the lowest of these as a cooking area where all the meals for the men could be prepared. Above that, the next floor was divided into two rooms. This was forced upon them to some extent because it was at this level that the very top of the beacon (where the beams were mortised together) was to be found.

'The floor area was limited as a result but the small rooms made maximum use of what was available. One of them was to be for the use of the foremen and one for Robert Stevenson himself. In it he would be able to keep all the plans and details he needed for the building work.

'At the very top of the cabin was the room which the workmen would use for sleeping in. Officially it was called *the artificer's barrack* (like the accommodation ashore) but as with the other rooms on the beacon, it was by no means spacious. Measuring across the room from wall to wall it was about four metres wide and the narrow bunks the men used for sleeping in took up much of that. But no one objected to the cramped conditions once the cabin was habitable. It was far more convenient than the ships and, after all, much of their time was spent outside.

'A cupola of glass, built on the top of the roof, let in a lot of light to the men's sleeping area and access between the floors was possible by means of wooden steps. As all requirements had to be met, they even built a little privy on the outside wall of the kitchen floor.

'The cooking area in the kitchen or *cook-house* was made of brick for fairly obvious safety reasons. A blaze in a wooden building of this nature and in this location would have been disastrous. Two flues had to be fitted up, one to take away the smoke from the kitchen fire and the other for the smith's fire on the mortar gallery.

'With so much to be done, the joiners worked on at this task over the whole of the summer. It took them all of that time to make the cabin strong enough to withstand the next winter's weather. The finishing touches and the fitting out of the interior were, in fact, not completed until the next year.

'In the meantime, work on the lighthouse itself had to go on as best it could and the men had to make do with living on the *Sir Joseph Banks*. If the time of low tide was early, they could be on the Rock by 4 a.m. to make maximum use of the daylight hours. When this was the case, and a landing was made before it was time for breakfast to be served, all the workmen and sailors received a dram, a biscuit and coffee before going off to work.

'Then, on their return to the ship, breakfast would be ready. It must have been most welcome. With such an early start it was possible, approximately twelve hours later, to land for a second time. However, if the time of that next low tide was sufficiently late, work went on by torch light as it had done the year before. It must have been a strange sight to see lights so low on the water.

'They found that the excavation of the foundation pit became more and more difficult as time went on. Not only did the points of the picks often break, but the wooden handles frequently split as well. One joiner was kept permanently employed fitting new ones in order to keep things going.

'Of course the deeper the men dug, the more water would collect in the pit at high tide. All of it had to be pumped out before the masons could restart and doing this inevitably took longer and longer each day. One idea which had been suggested in anticipation of just this problem was the building of a cast iron cofferdam about one and a half metres high around the site. Such structures were used in harbour or similar types of building work. The idea got no further, however. It was soon abandoned as being impractical and they decided to make do with the wooden pumps instead.

'Nevertheless, some of the irregularities on the rock surface were filled in with mortar to try and ease the task. Parts of the edges of the foundation pit were also built up in an attempt to keep out the sea while the men worked. The little walls for this were made of stone chips and mortar and were anything up to four hundred and fifty seven millimetres high. A small sluice was even fitted in one of them to allow the water to drain away.

'Even so, with the foundation pit measuring almost thirteen metres in diameter it could take anything up to half an hour to clear completely of water in the early stages and later on it sometimes took two hours or more. They needed twenty men to man each pump because it all had to be done manually. With so many now on the Rock, there were occasions when it almost seemed crowded.

'But things were beginning to look quite positive. Back at the workyard the first course of stone blocks had been completed. By the beginning of June they were ready to be shipped to the Rock whenever they were required.

'Problems in obtaining the size of stones they wanted had meant that this first course was not as thick as they might have liked. A thicker course took more or less the same time to cut to shape or lay in place as a thinner one. But it had the advantage that a smaller number of courses were needed to get out of the reach of the tide.

'Fortunately, new granite quarries near Peterhead had made it easier to find suitable blocks and there was now every likelihood that the first three courses of the lighthouse would be ready for building during the summer months.

'As had been the case the year before, there were times when spells of bad weather interrupted work for a day or two. During one storm which suddenly blew up the tender *Sir Joseph Banks* broke free of her moorings but fortunately all the workmen were on board. Her captain, David Taylor, had to give orders to set sail and head for the safety of the Firth of Forth.

'When the ship docked at Leith, the men took advantage of the welcome opportunity to stretch their legs on dry land. Unfortunately the state of their clothes left a great deal to be desired after having been at the Rock for some time. They set sail again as soon as it was possible to do so but lack of wind then forced them to anchor off Anstruther. It was to be yet another twenty four hours before they finally managed to return to their moorings.

'Now that they all knew the Rock so well, it was possible to row to it in most conditions. Even fog was not normally a problem. On one occasion, when a mist came in between the morning and evening tides, the boats were guided back to the Rock by the sound of the blacksmith's hammer working on the anvil.

'It was quite obvious how important sound was in that kind of weather and this would also be the case once the lighthouse was in operation. The lighthouse plans allowed for two large, cast iron bells to be ordered which could be tolled when necessary, like the one on the floating light.

'The new boats of the *Sir Joseph Banks* were found to be a mixed blessing in rowing backwards and forwards to work. They certainly helped carry more men at a time but they tended to be more difficult to pull in a heavy swell. In the confined inlets near the Rock, the larger oars also had a habit of becoming tangled up with seaweed or pieces of sandstone which jutted out from the rest of the rock surface.

'Work on the foundation pit, however, was increasingly affected as the time of the neap tides approached. It became more and more difficult to continue with the operations there and eventually work had to be abandoned completely because the foundation pit was never free of water.

'The construction of the railways was able to continue for a while on the higher parts of the Rock but even that had to stop in the end. As no-one could get any work done until the state of the tide changed, everyone sailed back to Arbroath to spend a few days at the workyard instead.'

CHAPTER SEVEN

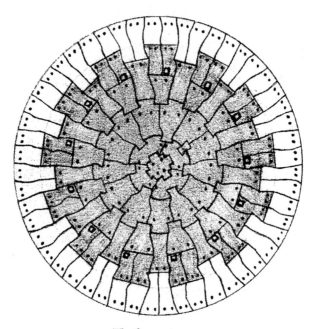

The first entire course

1808:
THE BUILDING WORK BEGINS

'By the end of June 1808 there were three forges at work and the foundation pit was well on the way to completion. Over thirty metres of the eastern track of the railway had been laid and there was still most of the summer to come.

'A series of good tides helped greatly with the result that the men were soon within sight of being able to measure the size of a number of stones that were needed to level off the base of the foundation pit. As these individual stones had to fit particular hollows in the rock surface, they could not be prepared before this point in time. Once they had been laid, it would be possible to start on the first complete course of the lighthouse.

'On the 6th July the measurements were taken for the first of the stones and a wooden mould was made of its shape. Stevenson then left the Rock with it and was taken back to Arbroath in a rowing boat. Once there, he headed straight for the yard.

'At the yard, two masons immediately set to work cutting a block of sandstone to size. Others took over as they tired. The squad of men worked on through the night and into the next day in order to complete the stone and get it sent off in as short a time as possible. No-one wanted any delay now that they had got this far.

'Three days later the stone was towed to the Rock on one of the praams which was decorated with flags for the occasion. As the railways were still not complete the stone was gently lowered onto the site at high tide. Those close enough to see what was happening, cheered. It was a great step forward for everyone.

'The ceremony to lay this first stone of the lighthouse took place the next morning which was Sunday, the 10th July. It was a fine bright day and at eleven o'clock all who could be spared landed on the Rock to see the proceedings. On the stone was cut, quite simply, the date

"1808". This was definitely one of those occasions when everyone was served with an extra tot of rum and a toast was made to the future success of the operations.

'However it was not just the workmen who were to witness the day's events. A party of sixteen people from Dundee arrived unexpectedly and joined the others in the celebrations. For a long time public interest in the building work was so great that many came out to the Rock in rowing boats to see the developments for themselves. The lighthouse, in fact, proved to be quite a tourist attraction.

'By the 26th July the last of the eighteen extra pieces of stone needed to complete the foundation pit had been laid. The whole surface was now level and ready to take the first full course of the lighthouse. That same day the *Smeaton* brought the first twenty stones for it from Arbroath and some of them were landed by the praams the next morning. Once again it was done slowly, block by block, at high water.

'This method was used as little as possible because there was always the danger of a stone being damaged in the process. But it was preferable to get as far forward as they could by landing the stones this way rather than delay everything until the railways were completely ready.

'What they did do to help safeguard the stones was land only as many as they knew could be laid in a tide's work. That way, none were left free on the Rock and there was therefore no risk of any being damaged by the tide. From experience they knew what could happen if the sea became rough and no-one wanted to leave anything to chance.

'The earlier stones which had been laid had been eased into place with poles but now they brought out cranes to the Rock to help make this job easier. Those designed for the wharves where the stones would eventually be lifted from the praams onto railway wagons were a very simple type – they called them triangular or sheer cranes. Even so they had to be fixed firmly in position in order to lift the stones safely.

'To deal with the stones on the building site they used a jib crane – although the workmen referred to it as a moveable beam crane. Two were eventually required in order to reach all parts of the working area. Each had an upright shaft six and a half metres long. A similar, although larger crane had also been ordered for the workyard.

'Great accuracy was needed in setting the stones in place because of the dovetailing of the blocks. The moveable beam allowed this. It could be manoeuvred in such a way as to enable a block to be lowered into exactly the correct position. And, by lowering them perpendicularly, the proper amount of mortar required was kept underneath.

'The upright shafts of the jib cranes rested on metal plates which stood either on the rock surface of the pit or on the stonework of the lighthouse. As the base of the lighthouse rose gradually in height, the cranes had to be moved and so could not be fixed permanently to it in any way. Instead, they were held in position by guy ropes which were secured to the rock beyond the building site.

'With the first of the cranes in position, the task of setting the stones in place with mortar and trenails began. Two holes for the trenails had been drilled through each block at the workyard. Now the hole had to be continued into the surface underneath. This proved to be the most tedious part of the work.

'Before the wooden trenail was put into the hole a saw draught was cut across the lower end and a wedge was inserted there. When driven home the trenail became quite firm. The top end was then cut flush with the upper edge of the stone, split with a chisel, and another wedge forced in.

'Sometimes they would get seven stones laid and trenailed during a tide's work, at other times it might be eleven. It very much depended on the state of the tide and whether there were any other interruptions.

'One such case involved another party of sightseers, this time from Leith. The men had come in their own yacht but as there was quite a strong swell that day they could not land using their small boat. Instead, they got a ride on one of the boats coming from the floating light with a cargo of lime, cement and sand.

'However the combination of the swell of the sea and the extra weight made the boat unmanageable. A large wave overturned it and everyone landed up in the water.

They had to cling to anything available to keep themselves afloat. It was one of those occasions when Captain Wilson, the landing master, had to do a bit of quick thinking.

'Fortunately they managed to rescue everyone although one man spent ten or twelve minutes in the water in what were really quite dangerous conditions. The lighthouse employees only got a soaking but their boat was wrecked. Part of the cargo was damaged and some was lost altogether.

'Despite this small setback the last blocks of the first course - totalling one hundred and twenty three in all - were laid in place by the 12th August. As it happened it was once again near the time of the neap tides and so with this important point reached, everyone set off for Arbroath in the tender. To let those on shore know that they had been successful in reaching this stage, they hoisted the ship's colours. Once again they were greeted with cheers as they docked.

'Unfortunately bad news awaited Robert Stevenson at the workyard. One of their workers, Hugh Rose, had been injured in an accident when a stone of between two and three tons in weight fell on his knees. It turned out that the carpenter's jack had not been adjusted properly and the man was permanently disabled by the incident. Because of this, the Lighthouse Board gave him a pension of £20 per year.

'Although still short of a number of stones for the third

course, they had managed to get enough to complete the second one. It was now ready to be shipped out. Unlike the first course which was three hundred and five millimetres thick, this one was four hundred and fifty seven millimetres thick. The granite stones varied from one hundred and two millimetres to one hundred and seventy eight millimetres in length and ranged from just under one metre to almost one and a half metres in breadth.

'This made them much heavier than those which they had worked with up till now and they were really too heavy to be safely landed at high tide. Fortunately, the railway track from the eastern landing place was almost complete and they could begin to land the stones at low water.

'On August 24th everyone set off again for the Rock. The good weather held and they were able to get the whole of the second course – one hundred and thirty six blocks weighing one hundred and fifty four tons – laid in only seven tides' work. To keep the supply going, the *Smeaton* had to ply furiously between Arbroath and the Rock. It was amazing how quickly she could sometimes get there and back.

'A second crane was now set up on top of the first course and this helped matters greatly. With two cranes in operation it was possible to reach any part of the lighthouse base without having to move one of them horizontally.

'However, just as the last stone of the second course was being lowered into place, one of the men, John Bonnyman, had a finger caught by a chain belonging to one of the cranes. His forefinger was almost severed by the accident and he calmly asked Robert Stevenson to take it off altogether! Not surprisingly that was one thing he did not feel able to do.

'Instead, they bandaged Bonnyman's hand and he was sent back to Arbroath in a rowing boat to the nearest doctor. His finger did have to be amputated but once the lighthouse had been completed, John Bonnyman became one of its new keepers.

'With two courses of the lighthouse complete, it was beginning to look more like a building. Part of the stonework was still lower than some of the rock surface but everything was progressing satisfactorily.

'As the third course was still not quite ready, Stevenson and those involved in that side of things returned to Arbroath on the *Smeaton*. The tender remained at the Rock for the other workmen who could still carry on with the railways and the cabin on the beacon. Once they had returned to port the *Smeaton* was immediately sent off to Aberdeen to bring back yet more granite.

'Work on laying the third course began on the 9th September. The *Sir Joseph Banks* had returned to harbour to collect water and provisions and so at the same time picked up the workmen who could now get back to the Rock. The morning tide was spent adjusting the cranes and preparing everything but by working from 9 p.m. until midnight, they were able to lay the first ten stones of the new course.

'With the building growing in height one very great advantage was found: it was possible to discontinue pumping. Removing the water had taken up a great deal of time at each tide before any construction work could begin. The fact that this was no longer necessary meant that the building work could move on at an even faster rate.

'On the whole things moved forward fairly smoothly. Once a number of stones for the third course had been fixed in place the cranes were moved up onto these. That task in itself took quite a time as the cranes were not light. But once in place, any workmen standing beside the cranes found that they were now nearly level with the highest parts of the Rock.

'Of course there were times when work had to stop if they ran out of blocks or if there was a particularly strong sea running. When the latter occurred it was not usually a good idea to try and land any stones. The only thing they could do was make sure that those already laid were secure. It was this kind of sea, too, which most frequently caused the mortar binding the stones to be washed away.

'There was always great concern during a spell of poorer weather that some of the stones might be lost or damaged. One day when it was too rough to land for work, Stevenson went out in a rowing boat with some others to check how matters stood. They found two stones raised perpendicularly off their bed by over two hundred and fifty millimetres! Fortunately they were still held by the trenails but it looked as if the stones were supported by stilts.

'This showed quite clearly how strong the force of the sea could be and also that the trenails were absolutely essential. Without them, the stones might have been lost altogether. When it was possible to get back to work, it was necessary to remove the trenails from the blocks and relay them for a second time.

'For as long as difficult conditions prevailed, a very careful watch also had to be kept in case any praams which were moored near the Rock broke free. The loss of even one of these, loaded with stones which had not yet been landed, would have been catastrophic. And it could happen. A raft of six Norwegian logs intended for the railways drifted away from the floating buoy to which it had been attached. It was picked up later on by fishermen near Anstruther who were paid £2 for the trouble they had taken in returning them.

'When any such spell of rough weather eased and they were able to get back to the Rock, it was a great relief to all concerned if they found most of the joints still full of mortar and that the equipment which had been left behind was safe. Unfortunately, boisterous conditions were to continue (to a greater or lesser degree) from the second half of September until the working season came to a close.

'The men found rowing in these heavy seas (or trying to land on the Rock) much more difficult than they had done before. And this was especially the case if they were pulling a praam loaded with stones. Inevitably there were a few close shaves.

'One particular wave caught a praam being towed, lifted it right up and deposited it on one of the ledges of the Rock. Fortunately the men were able to get it off again without too much damage being done and the cargo was, in due course, landed safely. But if it hadn't been for the efforts of the landing master and his crew and for the experience everyone had gained in how to approach the landing places over the two years of work out there, they would not have been able to carry on at all.

'On days when it was too impractical to land any further stones, the men kept going where they could. There were still things like trenail holes to be bored or the laying of more railway track. The one from the western landing place was much longer than that on the eastern side of the Rock and as a result was going to take far longer to complete. The joiners, too, were still busily working away on the wooden framing of the cabin on the beacon.

'But there was great pressure now on everyone to get the rest of the third course laid. There was no way that they could leave it partially completed over the winter because in that state it was more likely to be damaged by the sea.

'Any variation in the routine was made use of. One day when the *Smeaton* was forced to leave her moorings because of the weather and return to Arbroath, they took the opportunity to load her with other necessities for the Rock. Although it was late in the evening when she arrived at the harbour, the men at the barrack were immediately called out and she was ready to sail by 2.30 a.m. to make sure that she did not miss the tide.

'That trip was to have a sad ending. When they got back out to the Rock about 6.30 a.m. that same morning, Thomas Macurich, the mate of the *Smeaton,* and James Scott, one of the crew, went out in the ship's boat to make the vessel secure. The sea was still pretty rough and while they were there the chain of the moorings broke free.

'The boat was overturned and both men were thrown into the water. Macurich managed to catch hold of part of the boat but the young lad – he was only eighteen – was drowned. Those on board at the time thought he might have been knocked out by the buoy because although they called and called to him he appeared to be unconscious. Before they could get to him, he was carried away by the current.

'Fortunately they were able to rescue Thomas Macurich but the accident affected everyone. They knew that the boy's father was in a French prison and that his mother had depended on his wages. The sailors employed in the operations, unlike the workmen, were paid quarterly. It was arranged that Mrs. Scott would receive a small annuity of £5 and that his younger brother would take his place. There was probably no alternative for him if the family was to have something to live on.

'The last seventeen stones of the third course were eventually laid and with that, building work ended for the season. They had every reason to be pleased with how it had gone and how the equipment had performed.

'The stonework was beginning to reach out of the foundation pit which they had dug. If things went as well in the following year, there was every possibility that the rest of the solid part of the tower could be completed.

'But they had managed to do this just in time. Another bad gale from the north east forced the *Sir Joseph Banks*, the *Smeaton* and the lighthouse yacht (which was also there) to head back to Arbroath for shelter. Although there was nothing more to be done at the lighthouse itself, the *Smeaton* and the tender returned to the Rock three days later. There were still loose ends to be tidied up and everything had to be made secure for the winter.

'The *Smeaton* began the task of lifting the moorings so that they could be taken back to the workyard along with the other heavy equipment. On the Rock they found that the storm had taken its toll. The beacon had not been harmed but the crane at the eastern landing place had been knocked down. Despite the fact that it was made of cast iron, it had been broken into several pieces.

'Robert Stevenson's responsibilities now took him round the Scottish coast to visit other lighthouses operated by the Lighthouse Board. He got back to Arbroath in October and went out to the Rock to see how things fared. The stones and joints were intact (this was a matter of great concern) and the beacon and the railways were also in good order.

'Having satisfied himself on that, a squad of men were left to check everything periodically, as they had done the year before. At the yard it was now up to the masons to prepare the stones which would be needed for yet another season's work.'

CHAPTER EIGHT

The state of the works in September 1808

1809:
MOVING SLOWLY FORWARD

'The weather during the winter of 1808/09 was bad. The winds tended to come from the east or north east and those always produced a heavy swell, especially at the Bell Rock. It was often difficult enough to get out to the floating light with supplies let alone attempt to reach the Rock to see how things fared there.

'Nevertheless the repair squad kept on trying and now and again they succeeded. The main damage done was, perhaps not surprisingly, to the railways. They were, after all, not so massive as the beacon or the stone base of the lighthouse and they stood above the level of the rock surface. One piece of cast iron from the track was lost completely and another was found some distance away. Each of them weighed over forty five kilograms.

'Thankfully, any damage done to the beacon was not serious and repairs were carried out just as soon as the men were able to manage it. The force of the sea had carried away all but three of the joists of the lower platform and on one visit some very large pieces of rock were discovered near the beacon's legs. Presumably they had been thrown up from deeper water by the force of the sea but they had to be broken up before there was a chance of them hitting anything and causing serious harm.

'Most important of all, however, was the fact that the base of the lighthouse remained safe and intact.

'At Arbroath the task of cutting stones for the next season's work continued. During February the ninth course was finished and part of the tenth laid on the platform but even at this late date they did not have enough granite to be sure of being able to case the whole of the solid part of the tower.

'Because of this, an alternative had to be considered which involved casing only as far up as the high water mark. If possible, though, they wanted to try and avoid this so a man was sent by the stone agent in Aberdeen around all the quarries in the area. One of the yard's foremen was also sent to Peterhead to buy anything there which was suitable.

'Mylnefield quarries had closed for the winter but it was still possible to collect stones from there which had been quarried the previous summer. Carrying all the blocks to Arbroath from several different locations was quite a heavy task for the *Smeaton* alone. So, to ease the problem, another sloop, the *Alexander,* was hired.

'But the winter weather was to make even this job dangerous at times. On one trip up the Tay while heading to Mylnefield for a cargo of sandstone, the *Smeaton* lost both her boat and anchor in some very rough conditions. With ice all round the ship, her Captain gave up any hope of attempting to reach the quarry and decided instead to try and make it back to Arbroath.

'While on the return journey they actually saw another ship sink in the distance and yet could do nothing to help. They themselves were being carried in the wrong direction – towards the shore. To be unable to render any assistance was a dreadful situation to be in but it was to be a pretty close shave for them too; they only just made it back safely.

'As winter moved into spring the weather did not improve greatly. There was one occasion when those on the *Pharos* actually thought even she was about to sink in some very heavy seas.

'On a happier note, the crew of the floating light had been able to help one vessel avoid the Rock. A Swedish ship bound for Liverpool had lost course completely. Seeing the lightship, they managed to come close enough to her to get instructions as to where they were and how to proceed. In the end they went on their way safely but it could so easily have been otherwise if they had hit the Rock instead.

'At the workyard they pressed ahead and got as far as the thirteenth and fourteenth courses of the lighthouse. But of course the sandstone masons had a more regular supply of stone and so were further ahead than those working with granite. Fortunately a new supply arrived from the north in April and that eased matters considerably.

'Other materials such as mortar and lime had also to be prepared for taking out to the Rock. Two extra praams were built at Arbroath to ensure a steady flow of stones to the building site and more ironwork was ordered for the railways.

'Although they had been able to use the shorter length of track from the eastern landing place the year before, the longer stretch from the other side of the Rock and the circular track which was to be built around the base of the lighthouse still had to be completed.

'One problem they had to overcome was finding the quantities of oak trenails required for the coming season. Some were eventually tracked down at a merchant's in the south of England but they were rather expensive. Oak was in great demand at that time because the navy needed considerable amounts to keep the fleet serviced for the war.

'Then someone heard of a large consignment of the wood, suitable for trenails, being taken from the Highlands to Perth. It was really supposed to be used for making the spokes of carriage wheels but some was purchased for the lighthouse instead. The fact that the wood was much cheaper than they would have found elsewhere helped keep the overall costs down.

'In planning for the next season, it became more and more apparent that the pressures on the *Smeaton* and the *Alexander* were going to increase considerably. Not only had they to get the stone blocks to the yard to be cut to size and then transport them out to the Rock with as little delay as possible but there would be all the other materials and supplies to carry as well. It was decided that the best thing to do was buy another vessel to help out and so the forty five ton sloop *Patriot* was purchased for £470. Initially, she turned out to be a poor investment.

'When operations were about to begin again the ship was loaded at Leith with a cargo of ironwork, buoys, anchors and other equipment. The port of Leith was close to Edinburgh where the Lighthouse Board had their headquarters and where Robert Stevenson had a workyard for his own engineering business. Although the *Patriot* managed to discharge everything on her arrival at the Rock, it was clear that there was something wrong with the way she handled and so she was sent to Arbroath to be checked.

'The verdict was that the ship was unseaworthy. This was a very unwelcome piece of news yet there was no alternative but to have her seen to. It meant, of course, that there would be a delay before she could be operational and there was also the question of the extra costs involved in her repairs. The matter was taken up with the former owner and in the end it was he (and not the Lighthouse Board) who had to pay the £80 concerned.

'By April 20th the *Sir Joseph Banks* was ready to sail for the Rock with fifteen men on board. They were to see to any preliminary work on the railways and also continue fitting up the cabin on the beacon. The weather, however, was not so easily organised. It remained unsettled and, after laying two sets of moorings, the tender had to return to the shelter of Arbroath harbour. It was just too rough for the men to land.

'They tried again the next day and this time were successful. Unfortunately for them (although they could not know it) the poor weather was going to continue for quite some time. Nevertheless, at low tide they managed to get a lot of repair work done on the railways and gradually progress was made on the circular track around the building site.

'On the tender was more wood for fitting up the beacon. Prefabricated units were unknown in those days and everything had to be done gradually, by hand. But those involved in the final stages of completing the cabin could land at high tide (weather permitting) and get a long stretch of work in each day.

'Stevenson arrived at the Rock on the 1st May and found everything moving forward. In the middle of the month they actually managed to get five whole days' work completed without an interruption and that was very welcome. The masons were able to spend around six and a half hours on the track fixtures at low tide while the joiners and smiths carried on for anything up to fourteen hours at a time.

'When this was the case, the additional payments for extra hours worked (which the men were given on top of their normal wages) would build up. It could mean an extra £3 each month for an ordinary workman and double that for a foreman.

'Because of this, any unwillingness which had been found in the early days to take a turn afloat rather than stay at the yard had long since disappeared. The sailors who helped received bonuses too, but theirs were paid in a lump sum at the end of the working season.

'Before any actual building work could begin, it was necessary to clear the thick layer of seaweed which had accumulated on the stonework over the winter. The masons then began the task of cutting out the square holes for the joggles in the top layer of the masonry. Normally this would have been done at the yard but they had wanted to leave the surface as smooth as possible for the winter so that there was less chance of any damage being done.

'The cranes were erected and the seamen brought out the other materials that would be needed. Storing them was much easier now because the casks of lime and mortar as well as the wedges and joggles could be stacked on the floor of the beacon house.

'On the 27th May the first five stones of the new season were laid but after a second day's work a heavy sea once again stopped them from getting out to the Rock. The *Smeaton* and the *Sir Joseph Banks,* as well as two praams loaded with stones, remained at their moorings. All anyone could do was keep a careful eye on things and wait.

'It was only a bad swell like this which did interrupt the work. Throughout the whole of April and May the temperature had never risen above 5°C yet the men managed to keep going despite rain, wind or fog. On the last day of May they even laid stones in snow showers. On the decks and rigging of the ships the snow lay seventy millimetres thick. Despite the unpleasant conditions the men worked on quite willingly.

'After landing on June 1st, they managed to lay five stones during the early tide's work. Those who had to return to the ships did so, while the others remained behind, as always, on the beacon. Then in the afternoon, before a second landing could take place, the wind changed and became so strong that the *Smeaton* was forced to run for the shelter of the Firth of Forth.

'The *Sir Joseph Banks* was made as secure as she could be in order to ride out the gale. There was no way Stevenson wanted to leave some of his men stranded alone on the Rock. In the hours that followed quite a lot of damage was done to the ship itself and one of its boats was almost lost. As night approached it was still absolutely impossible to make any attempt to reach the others.

'Those on the tender were sick with worry. The rolling and pitching of the ship made it unpleasant enough for them but how on earth were the men on the beacon managing? The final work on the cabin had not yet been completed. There was no proper fireplace, no bedding and only a small stock of food and water.

'Throughout the night Stevenson kept checking with the officer on watch to see if the weather was improving at all. By 6 a.m. Captain Wilson thought it might just be easing slightly and at 9 o'clock he set off to try and reach the Rock in a well manned boat. With him he took some hot food and a kettle full of mulled port wine. The men on the beacon had had no proper food for many hours.

'To their great relief they found their friends safe and well. During the night they had managed to keep a small fire of sorts going and they had made use of some old sails to give additional protection from the spray from the sea.

'The foremen, Peter Logan and Francis Watt, insisted that they had not been too concerned about the danger in which they had found themselves. One of the joiners,

James Glen (a man with a very varied career behind him) had helped keep their spirits up by telling them stories of his past escapades. Nevertheless, they were quite happy to head back to the tender with the others and what a welcome they received when they got there!

'Once they were warm and dry the men were able to relate what damage had been done on the Rock during the storm. Three stones had been partially lifted but were still held by their trenails and one of the cranes had been broken. At high tide, the sea had washed away part of the mortar gallery taking some lime and other supplies with it. They had managed to save the rest of the material and were certain that the main structures were intact.

'Content that his men were once again safely on board, Stevenson took some others back to the Rock to relay the three stones and to check everything else. The men had been quite correct. Two of the four legs of the crane at the landing place had been broken into several pieces but fortunately the one on the building site was still safe.

'With no sign that the weather was going to improve rapidly, the *Sir Joseph Banks* set sail for Arbroath. How the *Smeaton* had fared after leaving the Rock the day before was a further cause of anxiety because she had been laden with stones. Fortunately she, too, eventually managed to make her way safely back to the town.

'At least matters were going more smoothly at the workyard. The sandstone masons were as high as the twentieth and twenty first courses and even the granite masons had finished the sixteenth.

'It was eight days before the workparty was able to get back out to the Rock. The three stones which had been relayed after the men had been rescued had to be laid in place for a third time. The sea had washed out the mortar before it had had a chance to set. Yet despite everything that had happened, those working on the beacon were still quite happy to remain there between the tides.

'Although the weather continued to be boisterous and there were occasions when they could not land, the construction work did move slowly forward. But time was precious. Every effort was made to ensure that the *Smeaton* and the *Patriot* (by now repaired) could sail constantly backwards and forwards with the stone blocks and other building materials. They would be dispatched by day or night to make sure that no construction time was lost.

'At the first hint of a change in weather conditions, however, everything was made as secure as possible. Even so, in the middle of June the men on the beacon had to spend a second night there but this time they were much more comfortable. They had proper bedding and on the whole felt that they were better off than those on the ships.

'That particular storm was bad enough to force the *Smeaton* and the *Patriot* to head for shelter once more, in this instance at Lunan Bay. The men on the beacon were aware of the house shaking at high tide and of the sea splashing on the mortar gallery but James Glen was again there and on this occasion they could tell their own stories of "Do you remember the last time …".

'The base of the lighthouse was by now almost two and a half metres high and it was possible to look out from the tender with a telescope during the storm and see the waves breaking around the crane which stood there. It was quite spectacular to watch the jets of water fly skywards but this in itself caused problems.

'The stonework was coming to that point where the action of the waves was strongest. Previously the blocks had received some protection while they were under the water. Now, due to the longer pounding of the waves, the mortar in the joints was more frequently washed out. Not all the stones which had been laid could be trenailed before work stopped at the end of a shift and the fear remained that a block might be washed away.

'Often the mortar had to be replaced several times and it was now that the new type of cement was useful because it helped protect the proper mortar. One trick which they also used in an attempt to protect some of the joints was to lay tow (a rough kind of cord or string) loaded with pieces of iron along them. Inevitably, with so much mortar being lost to the sea, extra supplies had to be brought out from Arbroath.

'The number of stones they were able to lay at a time varied enormously. It could be none, as few as four or as many as eighteen. The quantity was dictated, in part, by the weather but also by how much repair work was necessary. Boring holes for the trenails also took up time, as did fitting them, or the wedges, in place.

'One day they actually managed to lay a mammoth fifty seven stones! When that happened, or for that matter when a lot of mortar was needed for refilling the joints, the mortar makers had a very heavy day's work ahead of them. This became increasingly the case as the base rose in height because more building time was available before the site was covered with water.

'After the lime, pozzolana and sand had been brought out to the Rock in casks, the mortar produced from them was mixed in tubs on the gallery of the beacon. It was a messy job because the white, dusty lime flew everywhere.

'The gallery, of course, was also the place where the smiths worked. They still had to mend tools or prepare bits and pieces for the railways and the forge had to be in operation when they were working. Although the sides of the mortar gallery were open, the heat from the fire could still be considerable.

'Up to this point there had not really been a problem in trying to have both activities take place in the small space available. Building time was, after all, limited by the height of the sea and the smiths had all day in which to get their work done.

'Now, however, things began to change. Because the hours in which the builders could work increased along with the height of the building, the mortar makers needed longer on the gallery floor. But the construction of the railways was pressing ahead as well and the forge had to be in operation for that. Confusion and congestion resulted and tempers became short at times.

'The smiths complained of the dust from the lime and the mortar makers declared that they were *"between the devil and the deep sea"*. Quite clever in the circumstances!'

CHAPTER NINE

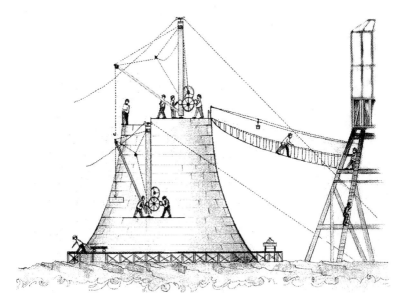

The state of the works in August 1809

1809:
WAR INTERVENES ...

'By the 25th June 1809 the stonework of the lighthouse was three metres high. This meant that it was tall enough to allow them to fix a rope ladder between the building site and the beacon.

'One end of the ladder was fixed to the beams of the beacon at the level of the mortar gallery and the other was attached to the lighthouse base by means of two lewis bats. It was a simple matter to lift these as the height of the building increased. They also set up a pulley system on a rope between the two working areas and with this could send across buckets of mortar or other light items.

'It all helped enormously as far as the building work was concerned. As long as the top of the stonework was clear of water, the men could move between the two sites even if the Rock itself was still covered. The builders as well as the joiners could now land before low tide.

'Because of this, and the fact that the masons could get their supplies via the beacon, the length of their working day increased yet again. On the first morning in which the new arrangements came into operation they were able to land as early as 3.00 a.m. and get over five hours work in with the early tide.

'The number of stones which could be laid at any one time was also affected. Gradually, that number increased. But even this work could grind to a halt if any necessary equipment was not to hand.

'There was one occasion when, by mistake, the *Patriot* returned to Arbroath with an important gauge on board. It was used to check the positions of the blocks as they were being set in place. There was nothing for it but to send a fast rowing boat ashore to retrieve it and so enable the work to carry on.

'As the rate of building work increased, the numbers of stones landed each day also rose. It could be as many as sixty or seventy. But then if the wind was fresh and from the wrong direction there were times when the praams could not be brought close to the Rock at all. The eastern railway was still the only one which was complete and it was not always safe to approach it.

'If the weather was good, however, they began to store a number of blocks near the base of the lighthouse to use in just such a situation.

'Other tides were completely taken up with trenailing, wedging, boring and grouting. They still had a bit to go before the tower was tall enough to be out of the range of the sea. Until that was the case, the problem of the mortar being washed out would remain.

'They found, though, that as the base of the lighthouse grew, it became more and more awkward to raise the crane from course to course.

'It did not have a large, heavy base to help stabilise it. Instead, it relied on the guy ropes which were fixed to the rock surface. As the height of the structure increased, these inevitably got longer and longer and became ever more difficult to manage. When the crane did have to be moved they had to call on the strength of all the men available.

'By the end of June they were at the stage where it had to be raised from the eighth to the ninth course. Once this had been done, the top of the crane would be over ten metres above the Rock itself. It was almost inevitable that a serious accident was going to happen at some point and that point was now.

'As they began to move the apparatus, the crane crashed onto the top of the masonry. The workmen, realising what was about to happen, scattered in all directions to get out of the way.

'Unfortunately one of them, Michael Wishart, stumbled on an uncut trenail as he ran to get clear and he fell on his back. As luck would have it his feet got tangled up in the wheels of the crane and he was badly injured. The others managed to carry him carefully back to the beacon where he was laid down on one of the narrow beds there.

'He must have been in dreadful pain. It was quite clear that they could do nothing for him at the Rock so he was sent straight back to Arbroath to a doctor. At first it seemed possible that a limb might have to be amputated but fortunately that was not necessary and in time he recovered.

'However Michael Wishart had been the principal builder at the Rock. Because he could no longer work, there was an important position left vacant. Despite everything, the operations had to continue and so another man, Robert Selkirk, was appointed in his place.

'As it happened that had been the second accident of the season. The first had thankfully been a lot less serious. A joiner had been hurt when a mason's pick had fallen from the mortar gallery onto one of his feet. It was not bad enough for him to be sent ashore but it did limit him in what he was able to do for quite a number of days.

'As far as Michael Wishart was concerned, his association with the lighthouse was not to end there. Like John Bonnyman who had lost a finger the year before he applied for, and was given, one of the keeper's jobs at the new lighthouse.

'Sadly, not all such incidents were to end so happily. A short time later one of the workmen at the yard, William Walker, was killed by a falling stone. He left behind a wife and two tiny children and they were given a small pension. It might not have been enough to live on but in those days provision was seldom made for people in such circumstances. For them, it would at least have helped.

'Back out on the Rock, the kitchen of the beacon was in full operation by the end of June. It was possible for the men to have all their meals there and so for any who were staying at work all day, cooked food no longer had to be brought out from the tender.

'The final touches were also being made to the rest of the beacon-house. The seamen prepared a quantity of tarpaulin to use for covering the roof. This was not quite what we think of as a tarpaulin today but was literally cloth coated with several layers of hot tar.

'It was quite suitable for making the roof watertight and was preferable to the other alternative, sheets of lead. They would have been much heavier to use and not so easy to work with in this particular situation. The rest of the cabin's woodwork was given three coats of white paint to protect it from the weather.

'Sacks of moss, bales of green baize cloth and red binding tape were brought out from the yard to complete the inside of the cabin. The moss was stuffed between the timber framing of the rooms to keep them dry and help stop draughts. The whole of the interior was then lined with the woollen cloth and the seams covered with the tape. They ended up not only comfortable but cheerful.

'By mid July the cabin on the beacon was completely finished. But even before then the joiner's squad and the cook, Peter Fortune, had decided to remain there permanently. They were far happier doing this than having what they called *"the continual plague of boating"*. It certainly showed how confident they were in the little building perched high above the Rock surface.

'There was another advantage to this arrangement. It meant that the rowing boats were far less crowded coming from the tender and as a result the task of the landing master and his crew was made easier.

'For Captain Wilson, the increased activity at the building site meant that he could no longer easily combine his duties there with those on the *Pharos*. So, for the summer, he left the floating light and concentrated on his responsibilities at the Rock.

'In his place, John Reid was appointed temporary master of the lightship. It was not a difficult task for him to undertake because, in addition to being a seaman he had from the beginning been the principal lightkeeper on the ship.

'It was his job to see that the lanterns were kept in good repair and that nothing prevented them being lit each night. The two men had worked together for a number of months and John Reid was more than able to take charge until the Captain returned.

'On the 19th July all the workmen, twenty three in number, moved permanently across to the beacon. This made life a lot easier for them and all their needs were seen to by Peter Fortune. He was another of those colourful characters who, like James Glen, had had a very varied life. As well as cooking, he kept an account of all the rations used and any expenditure made. He also acted as steward, first aid man and barber when necessary.

'Now that they were staying on the Rock, the men were able to get a lot more work done each day. They were helped, too, by the marvellous fact that the building was no longer covered by the sea at a neap tide. It was high enough for them to continue without interruption. When that happened for the first time the flags were hoisted, a three gun salute was fired and everyone was given their much deserved extra glass of rum.

'With the building work so far on, the beacon habitable and only the western railway to be completed, Robert Stevenson left the Rock and visited Shotts to see about the construction of a new crane he had designed. As things progressed they would need one that no longer had to rely on the awkward guy ropes for support.

'Although the men on the Rock found that they could now sometimes get in as many as sixteen hours work each day, they could no longer carry on at night. The torches they used were very simple ones with a naked flame. In the early days the foundation pit had given some shelter from the wind but with the height of the stonework increasing rapidly, this protection was lost. The site became more and more exposed and as a result the torches were often blown out.

'Then, on the 22nd July, the Napoleonic War once again disrupted everything. Word came from Lachlan Kennedy at the yard that the Government had placed an embargo on all shipping at every port in Great Britain because of the intended expedition to Walcheren. It meant that the *Patriot* and the *Smeaton* were confined to Arbroath harbour.

'What the British Government had decided to do was to send a force of forty thousand men to attack Antwerp and thus hopefully weaken Napoleon. The army did land at Walcheren and managed to capture Flushing but not Antwerp itself. Most of the force had, in fact, to be recalled three months later and so ultimately the plan failed.

'The effects of the embargo on the Bell Rock operations were potentially very serious. Without the two ships they could neither get materials out to the Rock for the building work nor food and other supplies for the men. The only thing Robert Stevenson could do (he was by then back on the Rock) was head straight to Arbroath to see if there was any chance of getting the ban lifted.

'No-one could deal with it locally and the matter had to go before higher authorities. However they were fortunate that the official in charge at Arbroath interpreted his orders fairly liberally. He understood the problems they faced and allowed them to take provisions out to those at sea.

'He also let them take out a number of important stones to the Rock. The embargo had come while the men were in the middle of laying the thirteenth course. Stevenson was very worried as to what might happen if bad weather arrived and the course remained unfinished. After all, they did not know how long the order might be in force.

'There was a condition attached, however. In return for these privileges a customs officer had to be on board the *Smeaton* or the *Patriot* whenever they sailed. This restriction was not lifted until word came back that the Lords of the Treasury had heard the appeal and had removed the embargo from all ships belonging to the Northern Lighthouse Board.

'The news was a huge relief to everyone but ten days of good weather had been lost.

'Although the operations had come almost to a standstill, those on the Rock had managed to complete the thirteenth course, even if they could go no further. What they had also managed to do was build a prop of masonry almost two metres high on the western side of the building.

'This was really just a platform of stones and fortunately all of them had been landed before the embargo began.

The prop was to serve an important function because they could set up another crane on top of it. Instead of lifting the blocks for the lighthouse an ever increasing distance up from the railway wagons, the blocks could be lifted in two stages. It made the job a lot easier.

'With the restrictions over, the operations were able to settle back into the old routine. At that point there were twenty four men living on the beacon. They were joined each day by the landing master's crew from the *Sir Joseph Banks* and another boat from the *Pharos*. In all, over forty men would be at work on the Rock.

'And at least now, on any occasions when the swell was too strong for the boats to be able to get there, work could carry on using the rope ladder to move between the beacon and the building site. Little time was therefore ever lost.

'The operations still attracted a considerable number of visitors, some of whom had been involved in obtaining the Government loan. Quite a number of the Northern Lighthouse Board Commissioners also made the trip out to the lighthouse while the work was in progress. Usually they brought a group of interested friends along with them. One thing was certain, everyone was impressed with the progress being made.

'Not all visits were intended, however. At daybreak one morning a large schooner only just missed the Rock. The crew were not local men and did not realise how close they were to disaster. The *Smeaton* was moored nearby so

Captain Pool was sent on board to help take the ship to the safety of the Firth of Tay.

'By August 9th, the nineteenth course had been finished and the structure was seven metres high. Twenty four courses were required to complete the solid part of the building.

'Due to the pressure of building work it had not, up until then, been possible to fix some extra supports to the legs of the beacon. Those who had been stranded in the cabin during the storms had been aware of a slight shaking at high water and it was hoped that the extra pieces of wood and iron would remove this.

'Work on fixing these began none too soon. They had not had the advantage of a particularly calm summer, weatherwise, and another storm was on its way. Although this time the gale was from the south east, the sea still broke fiercely around the building and the beacon.

'Twelve of the men living on the Rock decided they wanted to leave and return to what they saw as the safety of the tender. Despite the hazard involved for those who had to row out to collect them, they were taken back to the *Sir Joseph Banks*.

'Once again the sheer crane at the eastern landing place was overturned and a leg broken. The mortar gallery also took a pounding and floorboards, casks of lime and cement as well as the blacksmith's bellows were all carried away. After the storm subsided his anvil was found at the foot of the beacon.

'As August went on the weather was kinder and the remaining courses were slowly but surely laid in place. They actually managed to finish the whole of the twenty second course, amounting to fifty one stones in all, in only one day.

'On the 21st of that month the *Smeaton* arrived from Arbroath with her last cargo of the season. She was decked with flags to celebrate and all the other vessels nearby raised theirs, too. Some were even found for the beacon and the building site. By the 25th August the last of the stones had been landed at the Rock and the twenty fourth course completed.

'This was a big milestone. The solid base of the lighthouse was finished. Despite all the worries they had had about getting the stones they required, the job was done. The top of the masonry now stood over nine and a half metres above the surface of the Rock and the stonework was visible at high tide. At this point the granite casing would end. It was also a good place to stop the building work for the year.

'There was always, they knew, the risk of more gales in September. Although the spray from the waves could sometimes rise a considerable height into the air and fall, with a crash, onto the stone surface, it was not likely to do a great deal of damage to what was now a solid mass of masonry of over fourteen hundred tons.

'The men began to make everything secure and carried equipment which was no longer needed back to the ships. Although the tender would have to return to the Rock again to allow some low water work to be done on the beacon and the railways, she returned to Arbroath for the moment and received a great welcome.

'With minor exceptions the *Sir Joseph Banks* had been away for six months and for the last four, few of the squad of builders had been ashore. Peter Logan, the foreman, and Robert Selkirk (who had replaced Michael Wishart as the principal builder) had never once left the Rock.'

CHAPTER TEN

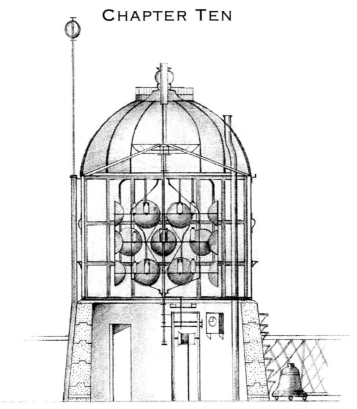

The lighthouse lantern

A LANTERN FOR
THE LIGHTHOUSE

'With the whole of the solid part of the building complete, there was now every possibility that they might be able to finish the rest of the lighthouse tower during 1810.

'Although much of the building still had to be constructed in terms of height, the tower would be hollow. They had already laid the largest proportion of the blocks of the lighthouse in place and would have nothing like the same number to deal with during the next season.

'In fact, just over seven hundred tons of masonry remained to be built. Double that weight had already gone into the solid base.

'As the prospect of completing the lighthouse came closer, minds had to be turned to the lighting apparatus and how to distinguish this light from others around the coast. The possibility of using coloured glass was considered and some experiments were begun at Inchkeith lighthouse in the Firth of Forth.

'In the meantime, Robert Stevenson set off in the *Smeaton* for Yorkshire. He wanted to visit the lighthouse at Flamborough Head where (possibly for the first time) red glass had been used along with clear.

'The man responsible for the lighthouse was the Collector of Customs. Stevenson met him and was shown around it. From the information he obtained it certainly seemed that a different coloured glass might be the answer. But they now had to find out which colour of glass would be most effective at the Bell Rock. It was very important that the lighthouse there was not mistaken for any other.

'From the windows of his home in Edinburgh, Stevenson could see the Inchkeith light. By attaching different colours of glass to the reflectors there, it was an easy matter for him to look out and see which worked best. To be completely sure, the *Sir Joseph Banks* was ordered to cruise offshore so that it was possible to get an idea of what the colours looked like from out at sea.

'In addition to red they tried green, orange, yellow, purple and blue. Only red was found to be really effective and that was the same colour as was used at Flamborough. If red glass was chosen, they were going to have to differentiate between the two lighthouses in some other way.

'The obvious solution was to change the shape of the reflector frame on which the lamps would be fixed. Flamborough had a triangular frame, two of the sides giving a clear flash and the other red.

'If the frame at the Bell Rock was made rectangular in shape, they could make two of the sides clear and two of them red. An alternate red and white signal would be the result. This was decided upon and the problem of how to distinguish the Bell Rock Light from any others was solved.

'The men who went back to the Rock to complete the extra supports for the beacon and do some more work on the railways kept going until November. They still lived in the cabin but some of the weightier items such as the anvil and forge were moved to the centre of the lighthouse building and the smiths worked from there.

'However as the weeks went on the weather inevitably

became more stormy and the men finally had to return to shore. The rope ladder linking the two sites was removed and all the equipment was brought back to the yard until work could begin again.

'Over the winter of 1809/10 the only ships in use were the *Sir Joseph Banks* and the *Pharos*. The others were tied up in harbour as they were not needed.

'It turned out to be yet another bitterly cold winter and the *Pharos* had to ride out some pretty fierce conditions. During one particularly bad storm, enough water found its way below deck to put out fires and cause a great deal of alarm.

'Work at the yard was affected, too. No quarrying was possible at Mylnefield from December to March because of the fierce frosts – the temperature fell as low as -8°C.

'Even at Arbroath many stones split because of the cold. This was despite the fact that they had been covered with straw and brushwood to try and protect them from the low temperatures. Having been damaged in this way they were useless for cutting as they were no longer the size required.

'At least work could carry on in preparing the other materials required for the new season. More lime from Aberthaw was burned and then reduced to powder before being stored in casks. Pounding the lime was not a pleasant task as it had to be done by hand on a stone bench.

'But less mortar was likely to be needed in the coming

season than had been the case in previous years. There were not so many stones to be laid and there was less likelihood of the mortar being washed out. As the building grew higher, the sea would not be able to attack the joints with the same force.

'Fewer trenails and wedges were also going to be required. There would be no real need for them once the building was about four metres above the solid base.

'One new item which was prepared at the yard over the winter was a wooden bridge to link the lighthouse and the beacon. The rope ladder had been fine but it had not been very stable. A bridge, on the other hand, would.

'Its main beams were over thirteen metres long and it was almost two metres wide. On either side there were protective wooden railings. They were essential if there was not to be a nasty accident and someone fall off onto the Rock below. In the centre of the walkway a wooden trapdoor was made which could fold back to give an opening two metres by one and a half metres in size.

'There were a number of advantages anticipated in having the bridge. One was that any number of people could use it at the same time. Another was the fact that the bridge was quite large enough to support a winch. It would be an easy job, therefore, to lift stones or other materials directly through the trapdoor from the railway underneath.

'Important work relating to the lighthouse, however, was also going ahead over the winter at a number of other locations, some of which were far away from the yard at Arbroath.

'It had been decided to use a different source of stone for the cornice of the lighthouse building and the parapet of the lightroom. It was to come, not from Mylnefield, but from Craigleith quarry near Edinburgh.

'Two factors were involved. One was that the Craigleith stone was not so susceptible to frost and the other was that it was very durable. Those chararacteristics were considered to be important because this particular stonework would form the very top of the lighthouse tower. Only the lighting apparatus itself would be above it.

'By preparing the stones over the winter at Robert Stevenson's Greenside yard, near his home, some other useful work could also be done. The new balance crane he had designed could be tested and an idea obtained of how it would perform on the Rock.

'Furthermore, the workmen would be able to fix some of the ironwork for the lightroom to the stones while they were there and before the blocks had to be transported out to the building site. This would help to reduce the amount of work to be done later on.

'Peter Logan and a squad of masons were therefore sent to Edinburgh for the winter. But once again they did not find it very easy to get the size of stones they were looking for. Those which were needed to form the floor of the lightroom had to be quite long and narrow in shape. Each of them had to run from the exterior of the building to almost the centre of the tower. Eventually, however, they were successful and by early March of 1810 the job had been completed.

'Other pieces of equipment which were required for the lightroom were also ordered. The cast iron window frames were made by the Edinburgh Foundry. These would form an octagonal lantern, giving an uninterrupted beam of light in all directions.

'Then there was the glass for the windows themselves. It was supplied by the British Plate Glass Company. The plate glass they needed for the lightroom windows had to be thicker than was then normal – over six millimetres – in order to be strong enough to withstand the strong winds and rough weather of a winter on the Rock.

'To our eyes it might have looked a little more green in colour than modern glass but there was no particular problem to be found in obtaining supplies which met their requirements.

'Items for the lighting apparatus itself also had to be organised including the sheets of silver plated copper for the lamp reflectors. They were to be specially manufactured by the firm of Boulton and Watt.

'The Watt of this partnership was James Watt, the Scottish engineer. He was the man who, according to tradition, was supposed to have had the idea of using steam as a means of power while he watched the lid of his mother's boiling kettle move up and down. That was not, in fact, true.

'What James Watt did do was make a number of improvements to an earlier type of steam engine developed by Thomas Newcomen. These changes were important in that they made the engines much more efficient. As a result of this, the use of steam engines became more widespread.

'In 1775 Watt went into partnership with Matthew Boulton near Birmingham. It proved to be a very successful venture for both men. Boulton had a large modern factory and could look after the business side of things while Watt devised new inventions and developed them. Boulton died in 1809 but Watt lived on for another ten years and so saw the lighthouse completed.

'In supplying the metal for the reflectors, Boulton and Watt provided a critical part of the equipment because its quality determined the effectiveness of the beam of light produced by the lighting apparatus.

'At this period in the development of lighthouses the large glass prisms which are now used to concentrate the beam of light from a lamp or burner did not exist. That idea was used for the first time in 1828 by a Frenchman called Fresnel. Technically it is known as the *dioptric* system and further developments led to the full catadioptric system which is the basis of all lighthouse lens systems in use today.

'Instead, at the time we are speaking of, they used what

is known as the *catoptric* system. In it, the light from an oil lamp was concentrated into a beam by a specially shaped (parabolic) reflector placed behind it. And there were two kinds of reflector available.

'One made use of a sort of mirror system. In 1777 William Hutchinson of Liverpool had produced a reflector in which a large number of small pieces of silvered glass were set into plaster the required shape. Although they lasted for a long time, this kind of reflector was not quite so efficient at its job as the alternative type.

'The other reflectors were made of metal and they were either covered with silver or very highly polished. Their one disadvantage, however, was that they tended to corrode quite quickly because of the intense heat involved. Nevertheless it was the metal reflectors which were to be used at the Bell Rock. They would need as strong a beam of light there as it was possible to produce.

'The metal content of the reflectors was very important indeed and the correct proportions of silver to copper had to be used. The best metallic reflectors around this time used over a hundred and eighty five grams of silver to each five hundred grams of copper. This was far more than was used in silver plated tableware of the period. For that, only about fifteen grams of silver were used for every five hundred grams of copper.

'Because of this high concentration of silver, it was quite a common practice to keep the cleaning cloths used by the lighthouse keepers for polishing the reflectors.

Some of the silver which had been rubbed off in the process could in fact be recovered and then reused. An early example of recycling!

'In Edinburgh, the task of overseeing the work to be done in preparing the reflectors and all the other equipment for the lighting apparatus was left to Stevenson's father-in-law, Thomas Smith.

'Although by now retired from any active duties as an engineer his great knowledge and understanding of lighthouses continued to be put to good use. He probably derived great pleasure from being able to help out in this way.

'In any large engineering work like the construction of the lighthouse a problem almost always crops up somewhere. In this instance it was to be in obtaining the red glass needed for the coloured flash.

'True red coloured glass at that time could only be produced in small quantities. It was used for such purposes as stained glass windows or decorations.

'They could not, however, produce the sheets of red glass which were needed for the lightroom. What they had to do instead was take a sheet of plain glass and paint each side with a gold compound. The glass was then subjected to great heat in a furnace and the whole process repeated several times.

'The final result was a good red colour on the surface of the glass, even if it did not extend as far as the centre of the cross-section. But actually managing to get the glass from the supplier proved to be very difficult.

'Several delivery dates were set, only to be broken, despite the many assurances given to the Lighthouse Board. They continued to wait in vain for the arrival of the glass throughout much of the following year, 1810. In the meantime the construction work was proceeding quickly. By the middle of October it had still not arrived and by then the building operations themselves were almost over. Stevenson and the others were inevitably very worried. Everything else was going to be held up if the glass did not arrive.

'In desperation, one of the Board's employees, John Forrest, was sent south to the supplier with orders to remain there until he had received it. This tactic must have worked because he arrived back at Leith from London on December 1st with the glass safely in his possession.

'Much earlier in the year, however, the construction work of the 1810 season had begun on the 18th April. By then the *Smeaton, Patriot* and *Alexander* were again in use and all the blocks of stone as high as the forty fourth course of the lighthouse were ready. Seventeen men went out to the Rock on the tender and one of their first tasks was to set the bridge in place.

'At one end its main beams were bolted to the beacon. At the other, one of the beams lay on what would be the instep of the lighthouse door while the second rested on a hole specially cut for it in the upper course of the granite.

'The men did not immediately move into the house on the beacon but went back to the tender at night. After being unoccupied for so many months the little cabin was a bit damp and musty at first. One day when they got out to it they found that the kitchen door had been forced open by the sea but it had only a simple catch to hold it closed.

'This had been done on purpose just in case anyone was shipwrecked on the Rock during the winter. It would not, then, have been difficult for them to get into the building and find shelter. Some food had also been left behind. From the cabin, of course, it would have been easy to send a signal for help to the floating light and contingency plans allowed for a rescue boat to be sent across from the ship as soon as it was practical to do so. Fortunately that was never necessary.

'Although new boards had to be laid on the mortar gallery, little else in the way of repair work needed to be done to the cabin. In some of the rooms, water had managed to get through the boards and discolour the green cloth slightly but it did not take long to get the beacon ready for occupation once more.

'Over the winter it was again the railways which appeared to have suffered most. As usual they had taken a pounding from any heavy stones moved around by the sea in bad weather. A number of blocks from the prop of masonry beside the lighthouse had also been scattered here and there.

'On closer examination it was discovered that some parts of the main beams of the beacon were not in such good condition as they had at first thought. They found that pieces of the wood had been eaten away.

'The areas most affected were those which stood directly on the rock surface where it had been impossible to coat the wood with pitch. Some of the beams had been partly hollowed out while others stood clear of the rock and depended entirely on the stanchions for support.

'But at least as far as the lighthouse was concerned, all the mortar in the joints had remained firm. No damage had been done to the stonework and although it was once again well covered with seaweed, that could easily be dealt with.

'No construction work could begin, however, until the new balance crane had been brought out and assembled. It arrived in pieces on a praam and the parts were then moved along the railway to underneath the new bridge. From the track they were lifted up through the trapdoor by the winch and then taken across to the solid part of the building.

'The crane, once it had been set up, had an iron weight to counterbalance the load being lifted. Everyone hoped that it would be a lot safer to use in the months to come than the old ones with the awkward guy ropes.'

CHAPTER ELEVEN

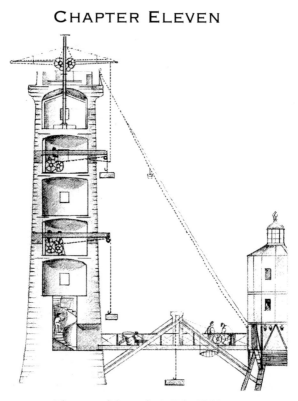

The state of the works in July 1810

1810:
THE TOWER GROWS QUICKLY

'On the 11th May 1810, the men began the job of clearing the seaweed which had accumulated over the winter on the base of the lighthouse. From the way it grew they could see quite clearly the direction of the heaviest seas.

'This was actually a very useful piece of information because it confirmed where the best location was to place the door of the lighthouse. In such an exposed position out in the North Sea the door needed as much shelter as possible. The logical solution was to site it away from the worst of the weather, on the opposite side of the building.

'The *Smeaton* arrived from Arbroath on the same day with her first cargo of stones for the building work – thirty eight blocks in all. Unfortunately, as on some other occasions in the past, the weather prospects did not look too good. The sea was rough and it proved very difficult to fasten the ship to her moorings.

'Nor did matters quickly improve. It was impossible to try to land any of the stones or to get out to the Rock. The men already living on the beacon were able to get some work done (such as cutting out the joggle holes in the upper course) but those on the ships had no alternative but to remain there.

'Eventually the wind became so fresh that the *Smeaton* had to head back to Arbroath, still laden, in order to make sure no harm came to her cargo. The *Sir Joseph Banks* remained at her moorings. From on board the sea could be seen breaking over the beacon in great sprays and swirling up amongst the beams below.

'So it continued for several days. The *Smeaton,* making a second attempt to get back out to the Rock, was instead driven south towards the Firth of Forth by the fierce conditions.

'Fortunately, the weather did begin to improve after about six days. The *Patriot* managed to get out with supplies for the floating light, the tender and the beacon. She then set off for Mylnefield to collect what would be the last cargo of sandstone from the quarry there.

'When a boat from the *Sir Joseph Banks* eventually reached the Rock they found everyone on the beacon safe and well, if rather bored! It hadn't taken the workmen there all that long to complete what work they could do. Once it had been finished they had found that the time dragged by.

'But things began to pick up. As the sea became calmer they were at last able to land the stones and the other materials brought out by the *Smeaton*. Everything was carried on the railways to underneath the bridge and, from there, the winch lifted the stones (or whatever had to be brought up) through the trapdoor.

'Any blocks were then carried towards the building site on little wagons. From there they were within range of the balance crane. The stones were still dovetailed in shape and, because of this, had to be laid from above as before. Thankfully, all the new apparatus appeared to work perfectly.

'Yet again the *Smeaton* began to make her speedy round trips to Arbroath. As long as the good weather held, she and the *Patriot* lost no time in picking up or discharging cargoes. On one occasion the *Smeaton* arrived at the Rock at 11 a.m. and by 4 p.m. had set off once more for the harbour. But then they knew that they had, as it were, to *"make hay while the sun shone"*.

'On days when the weather was poor it was all very different. Sometimes it was only Captain Wilson's skill which made it possible to land any stones at all. It was his crew who had to transport everything to the Rock. They could be completely soaked by the spray and were often exhausted from pulling the loaded praams against the swell of the sea.

'The first courses to be laid were for the staircase well. It would lead up into the main body of the lighthouse. There were still a considerable number of stones to be set in place for each course but the centre was now hollow. The stone steps themselves were to be fitted later on.

'It was amazing how quickly the stonework now grew in height. In less than ten days from the landing of the first stones, they were ready to set the lintel of the doorway in place. However, just as they were about to do this, part of the balance crane broke with the weight.

'Thankfully no-one was hurt but everything ground to a halt. Without the crane they could do nothing and, although the necessary repairs were carried out as quickly as possible, three days of work were lost. Unfortunately, they were also three days of good weather.

'Eventually the lintel was secured and from that point the building took on a new character. It really did begin to look like a lighthouse.

'By the 5th June the thirty eighth course had been

finished and the staircase well was complete. Here, because the stonework was above the range of any normal sea, the trenailing and wedging could end. That in itself would save a great deal of time.

'At this point, too, the thickness of the lighthouse walls was reduced from one and three quarter metres to just under a metre. This left a kind of bench at the top of the staircase. It would later be used as a store for such things as water cisterns, fuel and provisions.

'In the plans for the lighthouse the now hollow tower provided space for a second store immediately above this one. Above that there was to be a kitchen come living room for the keepers and on the next floor a bedroom. The final room located within the tower was a library. As it would be mainly for the use of visitors, it was also called *the stranger's room*. Only the lightroom would be above it.

'For this season, a day's work on the Bell Rock counted as nine hours. They were, after all, no longer affected by high and low water as far as construction work was concerned. There had been one or two changes of staff but on the whole most of the men wanted to continue with the operations and see everything reach a conclusion.

'There were now between twenty six and thirty one workmen permanently on the Rock although they were once again joined at low water by the landing master's crew of twelve to fifteen sailors. To sleep so many on the beacon meant that the bunks had to be five tiers high, allowing only about half a metre of headroom for each man. The widest distance between the beds was not much more than two and a half metres so conditions were, to say the least, a bit cramped.

'The men accepted the arrangements; they were not particularly unusual for the period and, after all, they didn't spend a great deal of time on the beacon itself. They could sometimes get in an extra six hours overtime by working, say, from 5 a.m. until 8 p.m. For every additional hour worked they received two and a half pence (or 6d) so that meant fifteen pence extra per day!

'In all, the ordinary workman could make over £2 per week and the foremen earned double that amount. Nor did they have to pay out any of this in expenses as all their meals were free.

'Now that the lighthouse walls were thinner a single block of stone was all that was needed to give the necessary width. As a result of this, there were far fewer blocks to be laid in each course. It was hoped, therefore, that it might be possible to lay two entire courses in the space of one day.

'But there were to be disadvantages as well. Inevitably there was far less space available for the men, the machinery and their tools. Consequently, the work could sometimes be held up. They also found that smaller items would quite often fall off the side of the building. If the tide was in they were carried away and lost.

'The men themselves were in greater danger, too,

should any of them fall from the tower. Just in case there was an accident, a small boat was suspended from the cabin of the beacon and John Glen (who had been a seaman) was put in charge of it. If anything happened and the landing master's boat was not nearby, this one could be lowered instead.

'In addition, a lifebuoy with a long rope attached to it was fixed to the bridge. It could always be thrown to anyone unfortunate enough to land in the water.

'Up to this point it had been the railways from the eastern landing place that had been used most of all. The track was only twenty seven metres long and was much shorter than the one from the western creek which was eighty eight metres in length. As long as the weather was moderate, the eastern landing place could be approached in any wind direction and using it obviously meant that the men had to pull the railway wagons for a far shorter distance.

'The western track was, however, now complete and only the final touches had to be put to the wharf there before a crane could be set up. Like the other landing stage it was made up of layers of large Norwegian logs raised to the level of the railways and fixed down with iron bars.

'But work on the lighthouse didn't always go quite as fast as they might have hoped. Now that they were working further up the tower it was not just stone blocks which had to be laid.

'As well as space for a door to the tower, window openings had to be left. The windows were to have wooden shutters on the outside which could be closed when necessary. These had to be attached to the masonry by special fixtures.

'The fixtures to take the door and shutters were all made of high quality brass. They were very heavy but had been specially designed to make it easier to replace any of the woodwork later on. Unfortunately, attaching the brass fixtures to the stonework did not prove to be a simple job at all. It took a lot longer than they expected.

'Such delays meant that the delivery of stones to the Rock sometimes got ahead of demand at the lighthouse. All they could do then was stack them at the western, more sheltered side of the building. The mason in charge of this, Alex Brebner, found he had to work up to the waist in water on more than one occasion.

'Once, unfortunately, the pile got just a bit too high. When the swell of the sea picked up unexpectedly at night, some of the stones were moved out of position. As the safety of the stones was of paramount importance, the obvious solution was to transfer them across to the lighthouse itself. They would be safe there, even if they had not been set with mortar.

'On the 14th June the masons were ready to tackle the forty seventh course. This was quite different from any of the others that had been laid before as it was the first of the *floor courses*. It would form the roof of the lower store and the floor of the second store above.

'All the floor courses of the lighthouse were composed of eighteen blocks of stone. Sixteen of these, long and narrow in shape, lay on the outside walls and projected in towards the centre of the room. The other two stones were for filling in the centre space later on. They could not be fitted yet because the hole left was needed for dismantling parts of the crane.

'Although wedges and trenails were no longer required, joggles were still used to help give stability to the stonework. The strength of each floor course, however, would eventually come from the weight of the stone walls built above it.

'This was all determined by the physical forces involved within the structure and it can be easily understood by imagining a ruler partly supported by a book. If a rubber, say, or a pencil sharpener is placed on the unsupported end, the ruler will fall. But, if an extra weight is placed on top of that part of the ruler which lies on the book, the far end of the ruler can support a greater weight without moving.

'Another factor to be considered, in relation to the length of the floor stones, was that the walls of the tower were not very thick. The floor courses were, of course, very heavy. Until other courses had been laid on top, there was a danger that the weight of the floor could pull away the stonework already laid underneath. Consequently, the heavier stones had to be supported in some way until further wall courses had been set in place.

'To deal with this problem the joiners constructed a wooden framework within the walls of the room underneath. It was able to take the strain for as long as necessary. The framework was, in fact, moved from room to room as the tower grew. By the time it was needed for a further floor course, the one below was quite secure.

'With the first room roofed, everyone felt that another milestone had been reached. It was yet another occasion to celebrate with an extra dram. Stevenson, writing home to his wife and family from his desk now placed inside the building, happily noted that the letter was the first ever to be written from the Bell Rock Lighthouse.

'With this important point reached, the balance crane was moved up to the next room. Dismantling it and getting it to the new level took quite a bit of time. The crane had been designed in such a way as to allow its foot to rest on the solid base of the lighthouse while the shaft could be lengthened as and when necessary through the central hole left in each floor course.

'In fact, they found it easier to dispense with the long shaft and just move the main body of the crane from floor to floor. To support its considerable weight they set the crane on two oak beams placed at opposite sides of the room. That way the stress was taken near the wall of the house and not near the centre of the floor.

'For as long as the weather held, the men pressed on. In

not much more than a week they were ready to lay the next floor, the one for the kitchen. But they were finding that every operation now took a little bit longer because of the ever increasing height of the building. The blocks had to be lifted further and further with each course laid.

'Because of this they found that they could really no longer keep two vessels fully employed transporting stones and materials out to the Rock. But both were kept for the moment, just in case any accident took place. That way they would have a reserve ship on hand and nothing could hinder the building work.

'Everything was actually moving forward quite quickly. Back at the Arbroath yard the task of cutting the stones was almost complete. By the end of June there was only the final course to be finished and already the first workmen were about to be paid off.

'It was difficult, too, to keep all the seamen fully occupied. They still quite regularly got ahead of demand in delivering stones to the site and with the railways now completed, there was nothing for them to help out with there.

'To give them something to do, they were asked to try and find anchors and chains which had been lost near the Rock.

'This quite often happened in bad weather but if they were retrieved they could either be re-used or sold. As an incentive the men were offered £5.25 for each set found, a sum not to be ignored.

'Unfortunately, the fact that time was hanging heavily on the sailor's hands caused the first and only unhappy incident in the whole of the operations. One of the men on the floating light became a bit disgruntled and it spread to some of the others. The cause was supposedly their daily beer ration but the matter had never cropped up in earlier years.

'Although he tried to get it all sorted out, in the end Stevenson had to dismiss two of the sailors. He also asked the others to think seriously about where they stood because, as their employer, he had the authority to dismiss them too, or have them sent to a man o' war.

'Men were still needed in the navy and those no longer employed in the lighthouse service would loose their immunity. The whole matter subsided eventually but it left Stevenson feeling rather sad and disappointed that it had happened at all.

'From past experience the good weather was not expected to last for the whole of the summer and, of course, it didn't. At times they had to put up with wind, rain, thunder and even lightning.

'On one particular day the wind was a fresh north easterly and it was accompanied as usual by a heavy surf at the Rock. Although the building was by then almost twenty metres high, the spray from the waves, flying up the side of the tower, could still soak those working on the top. And the water itself rose as high as the entrance door.

'The experiences of the men building the Eddystone

light had prepared them for something of this sort but it was far worse than they might normally have expected over a summer season.

'Naturally, if conditions became too rough, work was stopped until things improved. No-one wanted to risk any lives on the narrow walls of the lighthouse. Yet despite the unpleasant spells of weather, the dangers of the situation and the tiredness they must have felt working in such a difficult location, the men kept going cheerfully. Perhaps it was because they could really see the results of their efforts.

'There were still hopes at that point in time that they might just be able to complete everything during the summer. But, in looking ahead, they had to play safe. The red glass, of course, had not been delivered and if any problems occurred in landing the lighting apparatus the final assembly work might be delayed.

'The most sensible thing to do was to arrange for the *Pharos* to remain on station for another winter. However, she had been permanently at anchor for three years without a break and some concern had been expressed about the state of her timber work below water.

'John Reid, the lightkeeper and temporary master of the lightship had also been a ship's carpenter. He was asked to check the vessel and say whether she was, in fact, sound.

'Fortunately, the report which came back was

favourable. The *Pharos* would easily stand another winter at sea.'

CHAPTER TWELVE

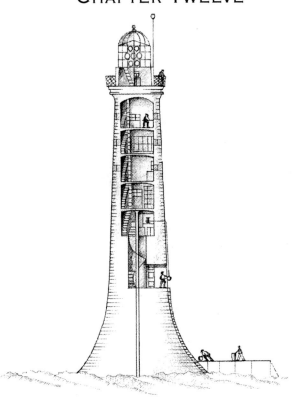

The completed interior of the lighthouse

1810:
THE STONEWORK IS COMPLETED

'At the beginning of July, a group of Magistrates from Arbroath came out to the Rock to see how things were progressing. The Town Council had been extremely helpful as far as the building operations were concerned and very much wanted to see the project succeed.

'The town and the Bell Rock had always been closely linked. Apart from the story of the Abbot's bell, it was said that after bad storms it was not unknown for some of the locals to row out to the Rock to see if there was any salvage to be picked up.

'Certainly the fact that the building work was being carried on from Arbroath was a matter of great pride to the inhabitants. It also brought more employment and extra business to the burgh. Having a lighthouse on the Rock would make trading from the town far safer. Arbroath had as much, if not more to lose from the Rock's location than any other town along the coast.

'The town was not a community which grew up around a natural harbour. Quite the opposite, in fact. It has always taken a great deal of effort to keep a viable harbour open.

'The reason for Arbroath's development lay, instead, in the Abbey (now in ruins) which was founded in 1178 A.D. by King William the Lion of Scotland. He gave to its Abbot and monks the right to create a burgh with a port and a weekly market.

'These were important privileges in medieval Scotland because they generated revenue and usually ensured the prosperity of the community. It was to be over two hundred years, however, before the first harbour was built.

'The then Abbot, John Geddy, and the burgesses of the town entered into a formal agreement to construct a harbour together at the foot of the High Street, what is now called Danger Point. In reality, the structure was little more than a wooden pier resting on boulders.

'It curved round towards the west to give protection from the kind of bad seas from the east or northeast which those on the Rock had frequently experienced. But the shelter available was limited and only a few vessels at a time could tie up there. Over the years that followed, the harbour required constant repair and it was certainly not liked by the seamen who had to use it.

'A severe storm at the beginning of the eighteenth century washed much of the old harbour away and it was quite obvious that if the burgh wanted to continue to trade as a port, a new one was going to have to be built.

'It was decided to do this at a site to the west of the original pier. An inner harbour was excavated out of the beach and grassland while a proper outer harbour and breakwater were built. This was the harbour the men of the lighthouse works knew.

'The entrance to the inner dock lay at its south west corner and it was near there that the burgesses of the town gave a free berth to the lighthouse service. They also gave permission for a crane to be erected there. This was a very necessary item to have, considering all the stones and materials which had to be brought in and taken out.

'The Town Council also offered to make no extra charge for the re-shipping of materials for the lighthouse. The fact that they did not claim all the shore dues they were entitled to, meant a considerable saving for the whole operation.

'A further example of the good relations which existed between the two bodies was that on the occasions when he was ashore, Robert Stevenson stayed with Provost Balfour at his house overlooking the harbour.

'Arbroath's harbour today is just a little different from the one that existed then. It was enlarged in the middle of the nineteenth century, a number of years after the lighthouse had been completed. Trade by sea had increased to such an extent that the old harbour was no longer large enough for the town's needs.

'They converted the inner harbour into a wet dock with a new, central entrance and a much larger outer harbour was built. What no-one, of course, could foresee was the impact that steam power would have on shipping. The development of steamships and railways began to change the old patterns of trade.

'As the size of vessels increased, fewer used Arbroath as a harbour and they made, instead, for larger ports like Dundee. By the middle of the twentieth century, Arbroath was left with only its fishing boats and the occasional merchant ship. Naturally, those who were able to see the lighthouse under construction were not to know this. For them, the building of the lighthouse was something which could only increase the town's trade and therefore its prosperity.

'Out at the Rock, the magistrates were able to see for

themselves that the work was moving forward quite quickly. One or two dared to venture up the ladders to the top of the building but most were content to remain lower down. After three hours there they set off back to Arbroath to cheers from the workmen.

'Because all the railways on the Rock were now complete, fewer men were actually needed there and as a result of this the number living on the beacon was reduced to twenty two. Similarly, fewer sailors were required in the landing master's crew each day.

'By now the kitchen of the lighthouse was complete and they were working on the walls of the bedroom. Building work sometimes came to a stop at high water if they ran out of blocks to set in place but there was still plenty to do dressing and polishing the interior walls of the rooms. Any roughness there had to be removed and a perfectly smooth surface left.

'On one occasion they tried to land extra materials at high tide via the bridge to see if it could be done. This would have meant that they could keep the building work going at all times and they would no longer be held up if what they needed was not immediately to hand.

'Although it was quite calm at the time, they didn't find it a terribly practical proposition. There were just too many potential dangers involved and so they had to accept that everything required would still have to be landed at low water.

'Of course as the height of the building increased,

lifting the stones from the wagons to the top of the building became more and more awkward. As the length of chain from the balance crane became longer it required much greater care to ensure that no damage was done. It would have been all too easy for a stone to be dashed against the surface of the building and one or the other chipped as a result.

'To make the job easier, once the stonework was about twenty four metres high another winch was fixed to the floor of one of the rooms and a beam was fitted so that it projected out of the window facing the bridge. With this in place the stones could be lifted in two stages.

'At this point in the construction work they were only about twelve courses away from the cornice itself and those stones had not yet been brought out from Leith. It was decided that the *Smeaton* had better head there and collect the first of them. Her master, Captain Pool, was also to be given the honour of bringing the very last stones to the Rock because he had been longer in the service than the captain of the *Patriot*.

'Before leaving for the Forth, the ship was loaded up with a lot of old, broken iron. There was plenty of it lying around the Rock, coming from broken pieces of equipment and damaged railways. It could all be taken ashore and used for scrap.

'As it was, the *Smeaton* would have to call at Arbroath on the way in order to collect James Craw, his horse and the cart. They could now be spared at the yard but would be needed to help load the stones at Leith. Stevenson and two of the masons went with them.

'When loading at Arbroath was complete and they were ready to sail, the wind was fresh and from the east. It was also very foggy. The *Smeaton* was supposed to call back at the Rock on her way south but without anyone being aware of the fact, she came closer to the Rock than was intended because of the poor visibility.

'Some of the sailors were suddenly alerted to the danger by the sound of the smith's hammer on the anvil. Horrified, they knew that it could only come from the beacon. There was just time to pull the ship about before she ran aground on the north west point of the reef.

'It was not the first time they had had reason to be grateful for the noise of the anvil and the *Smeaton* would almost certainly have been wrecked otherwise. Those on the Rock got quite a shock when the vessel suddenly appeared so close to them, apparently out of nowhere. But as she moved clear they waved to everyone on board, visibly showing their own relief at her narrow escape.

'Thankfully the fog cleared and with the fresh wind, the *Smeaton* made the thirty eight mile journey in only six hours. At the building site they were not so fortunate. With the wind came a heavy swell which brought work to a halt for two days.

'Part of the mortar gallery was once again washed away and the sea ran so high that it was impossible to cross the bridge between the beacon and the building. Great quantities of water broke over the lighthouse walls, despite their height, and came tumbling down through the rooms and out of the entrance door!

'The very last course of stonework to be completed at the Arbroath yard was finished on the 6th July. All that remained to be dressed there were the steps of the staircase and that was a job which would be left for the principal masons on their return from the Rock. The steps could not be set in place until the end, after parts of the balance crane and any other bulky apparatus had been removed.

'Traditionally, those involved in a major work of this kind enjoyed what was called a *finishing pint* together. Organising something of this nature, however, was not going to be very easy with some of the workmen still fully occupied offshore. So instead, a sum of five guineas (£5.25) was left in David Logan's charge and a dance was held at the barrack.

'Friends and girlfriends were invited to it but amidst the celebrations there was a touch of sadness, too. The men had lived and worked together there for several years. Many of the younger ones had also attended night school to improve their qualifications. Now their steady, regular job was finished and they would have to look elsewhere for employment. Everyone was aware that something special had come to an end.

'On the other hand Robert Stevenson, who was in Edinburgh seeing to the transportation of the final stonework, had a fascinating meeting. John Smeaton's only daughter, Mrs. Dickson, was visiting the city.

'She was able to look round the Greenside yard and also go on board the *Smeaton* which, of course, had been named after her father. As she knew a great deal about his work on the Eddystone Rock, it was a delight to her to hear, at first hand, all about the new lighthouse being built.

'Back on the Bell Rock the seventy second course was laid in place and yet another winch was set up on the bedroom floor. The whole operation of moving the stones was going ahead relatively smoothly.

'After being brought ashore at the two landing stages and taken along the railways, the individual blocks were first of all lifted up onto the bridge. Once there, they were hooked onto the chain of the winch on the storeroom floor and lifted so far up the side of the building. The process was repeated with the chain of the winch on the bedroom floor and by then the stones were high enough to be within reach of the balance crane on the top of the tower.

'On July 9th the *Patriot* was loaded up at Arbroath with materials and provisions for the Rock. On board as well was the very last cargo of stones from the yard there. Word of this soon got around the town and a large number of people congregated on the quayside to see the ship leave with the evening tide.

'Once again all the ships in the harbour were decked

with flags. They had celebrated the beginning of the operations a few years before and as the lighthouse was well on the way to being finished, there was even more reason to do the same now.

'A few days later those very stones were set in place on the lighthouse, completing the eightieth course. They formed part of the walls of the library. The next course would consist of twelve stones from Craigleith.

'The first of these were then lifted up by the winches and crane. A groove seventy six millimetres wide and one hundred and two millimetres deep had been cut in the top of this course. Once the blocks were in place a flat iron bar was laid into the groove and the metal was surrounded with molten lead. This was done to protect the iron from moisture because if rusting occurred it was a potential source of weakness.

'The reason for the iron bar being placed in the groove was to give additional strength. The weight of the cornice above was going to be considerable and this was a means of providing extra support to what were, in proportion, the relatively thin walls of the tower. Later on, there would also be the added weight of the lighting mechanism itself.

'The next course due to be laid formed part of the dome (or ceiling) of the library. Unfortunately, the Craigleith stones did not prove to be as easy to work with as the others had been. They were not only more difficult to set in place but also tended to be more easily damaged.

'Nevertheless, the last of them were now on their way from Leith. The *Smeaton* had sailed from there with the kind of send-off the *Patriot* had had at Arbroath. It was obviously not only the Arbroath folk who were following the building operations with avid interest. Furthermore, many visitors still braved the journey to the lighthouse in rowing boats.

'At the Rock they wrapped the Craigleith stones in canvas matting to try and protect them while they were being moved. The fact that the sea was rather choppy at the time did not help matters. With everyone trying to be especially careful, it was another occasion when the landing master's crew had to work waist deep in water.

'The sixteen long narrow blocks which made up the balcony and the lightroom floor were particularly difficult to deal with. It rained heavily while the men were working on them so they must have found it very uncomfortable up on top of the tower. Their only consolation was that there was no strong wind to complicate matters.

'Once that course was complete – it was the eighty fifth of the lighthouse – all that remained were the courses that would form the parapet wall of the lightroom. On top of them the lightroom windows would be fixed but at least the men involved in that work would have a balcony to walk round and not just the narrow wall.

'On the 29th July Captain Wilson and his crew brought out the final stones to the Rock. The praam which had carried the first stone also carried the last and once again it was decorated with flags to celebrate the occasion. All the ships anchored nearby hoisted their colours, too. It was quite a spectacle.

'Fortunately the weather that day was good and as the praam approached the landing place the men standing there gave three, very hearty cheers. It was a special moment for everyone.

'Those very stones were laid the next day. The last one to be set in place, by Robert Stevenson himself, was the lintel of the lightroom door. With the ninetieth and last course of the lighthouse complete, the building stood just over thirty one metres high.

'Now it was a question of beginning to clear up what was no longer needed until the lighting apparatus itself could be installed. The landing master's crew had, in fact, already begun this task because over the previous few days they had had less to do in the way of landing stones and materials. It helped to fill their time.

'The workmen, too, began to clear any rubbish or timber from the rooms of the lighthouse and they dismantled any machinery that was no longer needed. It was taken back to the tender. Some of the men went across to the beacon and once again coated the beams with tar so that they would withstand yet another winter on the Rock.

'The foot and shaft of the balance crane were removed through the holes left in the floors for that purpose but the rest of it remained supported on beams on top of the walls of the lightroom. The lifting gear was still needed to lay the centre stones in all the floors and later on the iron window frames would have to be hoisted into position.

'By the beginning of August the last floor stone was in place. For the moment there was not much more that the men could do and they were all at a bit of a loss. For several years their lives had been dominated by the need to get the lighthouse tower built. Now that it was complete there was almost a sense of anticlimax.

'Arrangements were made for everyone to return ashore until the next stage could begin. Many of the men had been at work on the Rock for several months and most of them needed to replace belongings which had been lost to the sea.

'They collected their few bits and pieces together and returned to the *Sir Joseph Banks*. Once there, Robert Stevenson thanked the men and complimented them on the marvellous job they had done.

'Back on shore, he invited the senior personnel from the workyard, the foremen and the captains of the ships to their own celebration at one of the local inns.

'It must have been a very special evening for them all.'

CHAPTER THIRTEEN

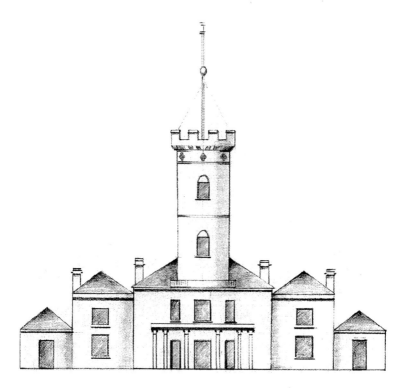

The Signal Tower

THE LAMPS ARE LIT

'In July 1810 the Lighthouse Commissioners in Edinburgh decided to buy a piece of land on the sea front just to the south of Arbroath harbour. On it, the accommodation which would be needed for those involved in manning the lighthouse was to be built.

'The masons who returned ashore after their work at the lighthouse was finished now began to tackle this job. The main building contained four apartments and, across the walled courtyard which enclosed the whole site there were another two cottages. Because the buildings were very close to the water, a strong sea wall was built to protect them.

'The lighthouse keepers, their families, the Master of the Tender and any seamen who served on the tender were able to live there. Each family had two or three rooms for their own use. Space was available for stores, coal and potato cellars were included and also outside *privies.* These would have used ashes because it was long before the time of flushing toilets.

'One other very important feature was included – a tower approximately eighteen metres high. Built as part of the main building, it had an uninterrupted view across the sea. As a result, once the tower was complete, it was possible to send signals from the top of it to the lighthouse and receive signals in return. Because of this the tower was called, not surprisingly, the Signal Tower and the name eventually came to apply to the whole complex.

'The masons were also given the task of enclosing a large area of garden ground a short distance away from the houses. Fresh fruit and vegetables were to be grown there for use at the lighthouse or by the families ashore. Whichever keeper was on leave had the job of looking after it. The garden was an essential asset at a time when most people still grew some of their own produce. There were no supermarkets then.

'As far as the workyard was concerned, there were still three years left to run of the seven year lease. The whole building operation had been completed in less time than had initially been expected. The owner of the yard was paid one year's rent in compensation for its early closure and the job of clearing everything began.

'But it was a case of *"waste not, want not"*. Anything that could be re-used was kept. The Commissioners did not have unlimited funds at their disposal and every effort was made to keep the expenditure as low as possible.

'The central platform which had been used for checking the blocks for the lighthouse contained a lot of good stones and rubble. This was taken across to the new houses and used for interior walls.

'The *Smeaton,* meanwhile, lifted any moorings that were no longer necessary and went off to Leith to collect the cast iron window frames for the lightroom. When she got back to Arbroath the twenty three stone steps for the lighthouse were ready and they, too, were taken on board.

'Peter Logan and sixteen men headed back to the Rock to begin the final work there. Not long after they reached the Rock and got out to the beacon, the good weather changed. Heavy seas caused the *Smeaton* to break free of her moorings and she had to head for the

Firth of Forth for shelter. In doing so she once again only just missed the Rock itself.

'Those left alone in the cabin felt very forlorn with no vessel nearby to help in an emergency. The spray from the sea fell noisily on the roof and the waves rose as high as twenty four metres on the walls of the lighthouse tower.

'The mortar gallery disappeared again, sending the hearth, the bellows and other equipment down onto the Rock below. Even part of the boarding of the kitchen was washed away.

'Although water once again swept over the bridge at high tide, some of the men took the opportunity (before it was at its full height) to cross to the lighthouse and see what it was like to stand inside.

'They were aware of a slight vibration in the walls when a wave hit the building and noticed that the spray was quite capable of soaking the balcony so far above. It even came over the parapet wall into the interior of what would be the lightroom.

'Fortunately the weather improved after a couple of days and the *Smeaton* returned. The men on the ship and the Rock signalled to one another and the *Smeaton* set off to Arbroath knowing that those on the beacon were safe. She needed to have some rigging attended to which had been damaged in the storm. While there, she was also able to collect the materials now needed for repairs to the cabin.

'On the Rock the men found the heavy anvil in a hole more than eighteen metres from the beacon. The hearth of the forge (which was not a great deal lighter) was found over sixty metres away.

'By the 23rd August they were ready to start lifting the window frames into position. As usual they were hoisted up onto the bridge first. While one of them was being set in place there, it began to topple over. Captain Wilson, in trying to save the frame from damage, was bruised on an old gunshot wound and he had to rest for several days.

'Despite this accident, the eight sash frames were lifted to the top of the building. Each of them weighed over one hundred and fifteen kilograms. What remained of the balance crane was then unscrewed and lowered *"in mournful silence"* to the bottom of the building. Its job was finally done.

'With all the heavier items now at the lighthouse, the bridge was removed. It had been found to have quite an effect on the beacon when a bad sea struck and could not have withstood a winter on the Rock. The old rope ladder was set up again and the timber beams were taken back to Arbroath to be used in the houses there.

'The masons completed their work on the steps of the staircase which led up into the tower from the entrance door. Robert Stevenson set the last one in place. With that done, most of the men returned again to Arbroath. The few who were left had to see to repair work on the railways. They also attended to the other bits and pieces that remained to be done in order to make the lighthouse habitable.

'At Arbroath, Lachlan Kennedy and Peter Logan were left in charge of the construction of the keeper's houses. It was time for Robert Stevenson to set off on his annual tour of the Board's other lighthouses.

'Then, at the beginning of October, the tender *Sir Joseph Banks* was taken to Leith to be dismantled and sold. Everyone felt very sad to see her go as they had all spent a great deal of time on her over the years. But the building operations were winding down and she was no longer needed.

'Of course there still remained the lightroom to complete. The rest of the apparatus for it was now ready and the *Smeaton* was able to take the first consignment out to the Rock. Also on board were James Dove and the other workmen who were to deal with this important stage.

'The first thing they did was put up a temporary rail around the balcony. Having ropes there made it a lot safer for the men until the permanent iron railings could be fixed in place.

'The fittings to take the sash windows were attached to the stone walls of the lightroom and the sashes themselves were then lifted into position. The frames were screwed together and the coppersmiths began the job of fitting the copper roof (or cupola) of the room.

'Once it was complete, a gilded ball was screwed into place at the very top. Through it ran the main ventilation tube for the lightroom which allowed the heat and fumes generated by the lamps to escape.

'The plate glass for the lightroom was landed safely to everyone's relief. Having been specially ordered for the job, it would have taken time to replace had any of it been broken. Once it was set into the windows and everything painted, the room was ready for the actual lighting equipment.

'Then, sadly, just as things were going so well, the only fatal accident to take place on the Rock occurred on the 16th October.

'Inevitably, as the men worked on through the autumn months the hours of daylight became shorter. On that particular evening it was dark by 7 o'clock so James Dove gave the order to stop work. Everyone got ready to return to the beacon.

'Two of the workmen, Charles Henderson and Henry Dickson, tried to outrun one another to the bottom of the lighthouse tower. They were young lads and by now knew the building well. Henderson led the way and the two called out to each other as far as the rope ladder.

'However when Dickson reached the kitchen of the beacon he realised that his friend was not there ahead of him. He had thought that he had heard something splash but not for a moment had he considered the possibility that it might be a man falling into the water. The alarm was raised.

'Lights were brought in case they could see any sign of Henderson in the water. Some of the workmen climbed down the legs of the beacon as far as they were able to but it was almost high tide. If he had landed in the sea there was not a great deal of hope that he would be found.

'A watch was kept until low water and every part of the lighthouse and the beacon was searched. It was all to no avail. The only conclusion that they could come to was that Henderson had somehow slipped through the rope ladder and been washed away into deep water. The fact that he did not appear to cry out would perhaps suggest that he was knocked unconscious by the fall.

'Quite understandably, the accident affected everyone. The men's spirits were very low and it took a great deal of persuasion from those in charge to get them to carry on at all. The fact that the nights were long and the weather was becoming more boisterous did not help matters either.

'They did keep going, nevertheless. By the end of October the main lighthouse building was almost complete and the lower rooms were more or less habitable. Only the main and inner doors remained to be hung and some final work done to the windows.

'Once the doors were in position, however, the rope ladder to the beacon had to be replaced with a set of wooden steps which could be suspended from the sill of the door. The position of the rope ladder made it impossible for the doors to close properly and so caused a draught through all the rooms. The steps, on the other hand, could be hauled up when they were not needed and therefore allowed the doors to shut tightly.

'Each of the windows had storm shutters on the outside to protect them from the spray. They could be closed by the keepers from the inside of the tower by opening the window frame. However the windows had a second, interior frame which normally lay within the woodwork of the window sill.

'This extra frame could be lifted into position if the weather was very stormy and so give added protection against the elements. It was really an early kind of mobile double glazing and was also fitted to those windows of the keepers' houses which faced the sea.

'With the completion of the lighthouse in sight, new keepers to man it had to be appointed. John Reid of the floating light was made principal keeper and he moved across to the building with Peter Fortune for company. Interestingly, John Reid's brother, Alexander, was still serving as lightkeeper at Eilean Glas on Scalpay, one of the first lighthouses to be built by the Commissioners.

'Inside the new lighthouse, things still looked rather chaotic. Water, fuel and provisions were stacked at the top of the staircase while tools littered the floor of the store. The bedroom was being used as a joiners' workshop and the men's beds occupied the library. Even in the kitchen they still only had a ship's caboose to cook on along with the utensils from the beacon.

'The *Smeaton* arrived in December with the rest of the lighting apparatus. John Forrest, having got back from London with the much delayed red glass, also came out to the Rock to stay for several weeks. As the Board's Superintendent of Lightkeepers, it was his job to train the new keepers and to ensure that everything was working satisfactorily before he left.

'The rectangular frame of the reflecting apparatus was screwed together and the lamps were attached to it. There were seven of these on each of the long sides and five on each of the shorter ones. In front of the latter were fixed the red glass plates to give the red flash. The lamps used were of the Argand type, the most up to date available, and they used spermacetti oil (a type of whale oil) for fuel.

'The invention of a smokeless oil lamp in 1782 by the Swiss scientist Aimé Argand had revolutionised lighthouse illumination. Before that, coal fires had generally been used and the smoke which resulted soon blackened the glass.

'In his lamp, Argand used a circular wick along with a glass chimney. The design of the system allowed air to circulate more freely. This meant that the oil burned more evenly and the lamp burned more brightly. It gave a steady, smokeless flame. With a reflector behind an Argand lamp its five candle power of light could be increased almost four hundred times.

'Although the reflector mirror behind each lamp concentrated the light into an intense beam, it was necessary to rotate the beam in order to make it visible from every direction. This led to the familiar revolving flash which we associate with lighthouses.

'The only method then available to turn the lighting apparatus was a clockwork system. It was really very much like a gigantic grandfather clock. The machinery was powered by a weight which gradually dropped down through the centre of the lighthouse and eventually into a well specially left for it in the solid part of the building. Unfortunately for the lightkeepers, they had to wind the whole thing back up again.

'The lightroom frame took eight minutes to make one complete revolution and the clockwork machinery was also designed to toll the fog-warning bells when they were needed. They were struck, day or night, at half minute intervals.

'Now that the lighthouse was well on the way to becoming operational, notices of this fact had to be placed in the newspapers and a specification of the light had to be drawn up. Shipowners and sailors would then know when the lighthouse was going to take over from the floating light and exactly what to look for. In the meantime, the *Pharos* remained at her station.

'The 1st February 1811 was the date fixed upon for the lighthouse to begin operating officially. That evening, however, Captain Wilson (who was once more in charge of the lightship) ordered the lanterns of the *Pharos* to be lit as usual, just in case. Everyone on the floating light stood on deck watching for the long awaited event. At last the light flashed out from the top of the tower and everyone on the lightship cheered. The order was given to extinguish the ship's lanterns. They were no longer needed.

THE BELL ROCK LIGHTHOUSE WAS IN OPERATION

'The *Pharos*, too, was now surplus to requirements. Sadly, like the *Sir Joseph Banks*, she was later on taken to Leith to be sold.

'The keepers on the Rock were not given an easy start in their work. A storm blew up with a particularly fierce wind. For the first three days the lighthouse was in use the men had to keep a twenty four hour watch with storm window frames at hand in case of an accident.

'The plates of glass on the windward side of the lightroom shook with the violence of the gusts. Although they were fitted with brass guards making it impossible for them to be blown out, there was a danger that the glass might be broken. Fortunately, it survived intact.

'Gradually, over the weeks and months that followed, the men on the Rock became more confident of their safety during storms although they were so far from land. Any early doubts or worries disappeared in time.

'The keepers continued to find that the most dangerous seas came from the north east because they broke close to the tower. Those from any other direction tended to break before they reached the foot of the building and the water then slipped past. Like the masons earlier on, the men were sometimes able to feel the spray from the waves on their faces as they stood on the balcony outside the lightroom.

'But eventually, if the storm shutters were closed and the double windows in place, the men were hardly even aware of a storm outside. Inside, they were very comfortable. The house was quite dry. This was perhaps partly due to the warmth given out by the chimney which led from the kitchen fire. It went up through the other rooms and then out of the building via the lightroom roof. But even the store-room (which had no such advantage) was comparatively free from damp.

'By the spring of 1811 the four lighthouse keepers had been well instructed in all their duties. As well as ensuring that the light was always lit at night they had to keep the equipment in perfect working order.

'A journal had to be written up, detailing when the light was lit and when it was extinguished. The keepers on watch were recorded as were the weather conditions and the times of the tides at the Rock. The tender's arrival and departure were noted along with any extra workmen staying there.

'Details of the provisions, water, fuel and other stores to

hand were also written up each day. They had to keep a good stock of spare equipment at the lighthouse in case bad weather prevented the tender reaching the Rock for a number of weeks.

'In April John Forrest finally returned ashore having spent more than three months at the lighthouse. He was happy with everything relating to both the men and the equipment. At last, after four years of immense effort, the lighthouse was fully operational.

'The Bell Rock was no longer something to be feared!'

CHAPTER FOURTEEN

The completed Bell Rock lighthouse

AFTERWARDS ...

'So that was the end of it all?'

'More or less.' Michael's grandfather stretched back in his armchair, aware that his muscles were aching slightly after sitting for so long in one position.

'The four lighthouse keepers who had been appointed settled into their new routine. There were always three on duty at the Rock and one on leave ashore. Normally that meant six weeks at the lighthouse and two at home but if the weather was bad they sometimes had to remain there for longer. It wasn't unknown for a keeper to have to spend three months at the Rock or five to six weeks ashore.

'They all knew there was nothing to be done about that. The *Smeaton* would arrive when she could bringing the relief keeper and any supplies or provisions required. All the heavy items were lifted up to the lighthouse door by a winch located in one of the stores.

'It was not all work. After their duties for the day had been attended to, such as cleaning the reflectors, the lamp glasses and the windows of the lightroom, the men were able to get outside and have a walk around the Rock if they chose.

'Sometimes they searched for fish to give a little variety to their diet. At other times they were content to read the books and magazines which were kept at the lighthouse or make their own amusements.

'Work on finishing the interior of the lighthouse continued for a while so at first they quite often had workmen there for extra company. Oak partitions and doors had to be fitted up inside, as well as wooden stairs linking each room with the one above. Cupboards had to be built and proper beds in the bedroom.

'There were six of these, to accommodate not only the keepers on duty but also any occasional visitors to the lighthouse. As space was limited they were again of the bunk type with three on either side of a central partition. They looked a bit like a tier of old fashioned box beds.

'The polished masonry of the interior was painted white while the roof and walls of the library were decorated with panelled oak. The kitchen, too, had to be fitted up properly as it was the room in which the men spent most of their time. A proper fire was installed and although at first water had to be carried up the stairs from the cisterns in the storeroom below, a pump was installed later on to make life easier.

'In the lightroom everything was made of stone or metal to ensure that it was fireproof. The only furniture there was a small table and chair for the keeper on watch. The importance of this measure was shown during the very first year the lighthouse was in operation. The kitchen chimney caught fire and the heat from the tube which formed the chimney cracked six of the squares of plate glass in the windows. These had to be replaced from the stock in hand.

'The cabin of the beacon was taken down over the summer of 1811 and the beams were removed the following year. The railways which had been built originally to transport the stones to the lighthouse were still needed to move supplies and fuel from the landing places. But they constantly required repair because of the damage done by winter storms. Eventually they were removed and a stronger, permanent track was laid.

'The spray from the sea gradually changed the colour of the upper part of the building so it was painted white to remedy this. The paint also prevented the sandstone absorbing any moisture. An external lightning conductor was fitted and later on, for extra safety, an internal one was also installed.

'The lighthouse had a big impact on all who sailed nearby. It also continued to attract many visitors. The normal rope ladder leading to the lighthouse door was not the easiest of things to climb. Anyone who could not use it was lifted up to the entrance by a chair suspended from the winch used to hoist up the supplies.

'Inside the lighthouse a book was kept in which the visitors could write their names and almost five hundred were recorded in the first summer alone. In 1814 when a party of Commissioners visited the Rock, Sir Walter Scott (the author of the Waverly novels) was with the group. Asked to write something in the book, he obliged with:

PHAROS LOQUITUR.
Far in the bosom of the deep
O'er these wild shelves my watch I keep
A ruddy gem of changeful light
Bound on the dusky brow of night
The seaman bids my lustre hail
And scorns to strike his timorous sail.

'With both the *Sir Joseph Banks* and the *Pharos* sold, the *Smeaton* (under Captain Taylor) acted as the tender for the lighthouse for several years. However she had been designed to carry stones and was not found to be very suitable for the job she now had to do.

'Because of this, a new vessel to serve as the tender was built at Leith in 1816 and once again named, appropriately, the Pharos. She took over the task of sailing out to the lighthouse from Arbroath every two weeks.

'The Signal Tower and the houses were also finished. Towards the top of the tower a small room was fitted out to serve as an observatory. In it there was a telescope through which the keeper ashore could look out to the Rock.

'From this room a narrow wooden stair led up out onto the very top of the tower where there was a flagstaff and a copper signal ball. A similar ball had been fitted to the flagstaff at the lighthouse and by moving them up and down it was possible to signal between the two buildings.

'This was important because in those days, before radio communication had been thought of, there was no other way of letting anyone ashore know if something was wrong. Each day, at nine o'clock in the morning, the ball on the lighthouse was raised to the top of the flagstaff if all was well. It was left there for one hour and the keeper at the Signal Tower answered by hoisting its ball.

'In poor visibility, when the ball was not likely to be seen ashore in the morning, it was raised later on from

1 p.m. to 2 p.m. If the ball was not raised at either of the specified times, it was a sign that something was wrong at the lighthouse and the tender put to sea immediately.

'There were more light-hearted signals, too. If the wife of one of the keepers was expecting a baby and it was born while her husband was offshore, a pair of trousers or a petticoat was attached to the Signal Tower's ball. That way he knew whether he had a son or a daughter!

'The keepers were also given a present of a pair of homing pigeons which, in time, bred. Some were always kept at the lighthouse and, if necessary, one of them was let off with a message attached. They could fly back to Arbroath at a rate of about a mile per minute. These were not regarded as *official* communications, however.

'Both John Rennie and Robert Stevenson continued to work for many years as civil engineers. Quite an argument arose later on as to which of the two men had actually designed the Bell Rock lighthouse. Certainly it is Stevenson's name which has always been associated with the lighthouse and the Commissioners gave him the credit of conceiving and carrying out the work. Rennie, on the other hand, did act as the consultant engineer for the project. The fact that it still stands today is a wonderful tribute not only to them but to all those who took part in the operation.

'The final cost of the whole project was £61,331 – quite a lot more than the original estimate. But as is always the case there had been unforeseen costs and the

Signal Tower complex had not been included in the original sum.

'Many of the men who helped build the lighthouse, like Captain Wilson, continued to work for the Lighthouse Board in the years that followed. Their names appear among those involved in other lighthouse works around the coast. Some, like Lachlan Kennedy, were promoted to posts vacated when others left the service. He took over from John Forrest as the Superintendent of Lightkeeper's Duties.

'Robert Stevenson's family, too, continued to serve the Commissioners as engineers for well over one hundred years. In all, the Stevenson family between them built more than eighty lighthouses for the Board and the connection remained right into this century. They were well known experts in the field and devised many improvements to the equipment used at lighthouses.

'One Stevenson did not follow in the family footsteps as an engineer. He was Robert Louis Stevenson, the original Robert's grandson. Instead he turned to writing and gave us such marvellous stories as *Kidnapped* and *Treasure Island*.

'The original lighting apparatus continued in use at the lighthouse until 1902 when a new system using prisms was installed. However, after the original reflectors, lamps and machinery were removed from the Bell Rock they were then installed at a lighthouse at Cape Bonavista in Canada. Other improvements were also made to the tower and equipment at the Bell Rock over the years.

'The tradition of recording the weather conditions, begun by the first keepers, continued. For a long time the lighthouse served as one of the weather stations around the coast of Britain. Each day it was mentioned on the radio.'

'And has no-one ever been drowned in a shipwreck there since the lighthouse was built?'

'No, no-one at all. To be perfectly accurate, though, the odd ship has still ended up on the Rock. But when that happened, there were usually other factors involved.

'The most famous incident of this kind involved a naval vessel during the first World War. In both World Wars, for the sake of security, the light was not in normal operation. It was only lit if ships were expected to be in the locality. Convoys were an obvious example.

'In 1915 the Captain of the *Argyll,* an armoured cruiser, asked for the Rock to be lit on the evening of the 27th/28th October. Unfortunately the message was never passed on because the lighthouse had no radio and heavy seas (once again!) made it impossible to deliver the message by boat.

'Lulled into a false sense of security by the fact that they could see no light, the crew did not realise that the Rock was so near. The *Argyll* hit it and sank but thankfully all six hundred and fifty five men on board were saved. A few weeks later the Admiralty sent a party of men out to the Bell Rock to set up telegraphic communication with Fife

Ness. Clearly they were going to ensure that nothing similar happened in the future!

'During the Second World War the lighthouse was attacked on several occasions by enemy aircraft, presumably in order to try and damage the light. Had that happened, it would have made conditions more difficult for Allied shipping in the area. On one occasion a bomb exploded a short distance away from the base of the tower. Apart from a few bullet holes and some glass being smashed, any damage done in the attacks was not serious. It was rather a different matter in 1955 when tragedy did come to the Rock.

'Helicopters from the RAF base at Leuchars in Fife quite often flew over the lighthouse and sometimes, if weather and sea conditions permitted, they lowered a bundle of newspapers or magazines to the keepers. These were always appreciated by the men on the Rock and the helicopter crews obtained practical experience in manoeuvring. Normally this was only attempted while the lighthouse keepers stood on the landing grating used for supplying the lighthouse, well away from the tower itself.

'On the 14th December that year a helicopter circled and indicated that the crew wanted to drop something. However there was a heavy sea running and the keepers could not reach their usual spot. The airmen decided instead to try and lower the parcel onto the top of the lighthouse.

'It was a very tricky operation to attempt and while they were manoeuvring into position something went wrong. As the keepers watched, the helicopter plunged, out of control, towards where they were standing. None of them were injured but as the helicopter crashed onto the Rock below, considerable damage was done to the copper dome and to the fittings of the lightroom.

'The three keepers raced down to the lighthouse door to find out what had happened to the crewmen. From there they could see the battered wreck of the helicopter, partly submerged and buffeted by the heavy seas.

'It was obvious that what remained of the helicopter would not stay there for long in the severe conditions and yet one of the men still seemed to be in the cabin of the machine. Somehow they had to try and reach him.

'One of the keepers fastened a rope around his waist while another held on to the rest of it. Going down the ladder from the doorway, the keeper watched for his chance in the rough seas and managed to get into the wreck below.

'Sadly the airman had not survived the crash and there was nothing the keeper could do. Carefully, he had to try and make his own way back to the safety of the lighthouse. He had only just reached it when a huge wave swept over the reef and carried what was left of the helicopter away into deep water.

'The keepers were left devastated but of prime importance was the fact that the light was no longer operational. That had to be dealt with immediately and a warning given to all shipping nearby. At least they could now do this by radio.

'Unfortunately the poor weather continued and it was several days before a temporary light could be got out to the Rock. Two artificers (as they are still called in the lighthouse service) came out to begin the work of repairing the lighthouse, helped by the keepers. The conditions they had to work in could only be called appalling, with freezing gale force winds and sleet.

'Yet despite all that had happened, on Christmas Day another helicopter from Leuchars visited the Rock. This time the sea was calm and the wind light. Over the landing place they dropped a canister containing a complete, piping hot Christmas dinner along with cigarettes and a bottle of whisky. R.T.Wood, the assistant keeper who had tried to rescue the stricken airman was later awarded The Queen's Commendation for Gallantry.

'In time a proper helicopter landing pad was placed on the Bell Rock itself and occasionally supplies were landed that way. But it was only used if it was absolutely necessary. For the most part the lighthouse was serviced as it had always been, by sea.

'Arbroath's close link with the lighthouse came to an end when the lighthouse families were moved to Granton, near Leith. This was where the Lighthouse Board's main stores depot was located and, practically speaking, it made more sense to service the Bell Rock lighthouse (along with others) from there.

'Yet although the lighthouse folk had gone, the bond between the town and the lighthouse remained. The Town Council bought the Signal Tower premises and for a time it continued to be used for housing purposes. Then, in the early 1970's plans were drawn up to convert the building into a museum. It opened in 1974.

'As technology improved, the opportunity arose of turning rock stations like the Bell Rock into automatic lights. For the Lighthouse Board, the problems and difficulties of maintaining this kind of lighthouse were reduced and the keepers no longer had to spend long periods away from their families.

'The Bell Rock's turn came in 1987 but even as those very plans were about to be put into operation, the dangers of working in such a location were once again highlighted. A fire broke out in the lighthouse, possibly caused by a leak in the fuel system. It was severe enough for them to have to call out the Arbroath lifeboat although ultimately the men were evacuated by helicopter.

'In the changeover to the automatic system the existing electric light (installed in 1964) was removed and replaced by a temporary one. Then, over the following months, a completely new Dalen optic was set up. The character of the light today is a white flash every five seconds and it has a range of eighteen miles. The red flash of the first system has long been out of use.

'On the 26th October 1988 the lighthouse was

officially demanned and today it is monitored remotely from the Board's headquarters in Edinburgh. The men may have gone, but the lighthouse continues to mark the Bell Rock as it has done for almost two hundred years.

'In fact the tower, virtually unchanged from the days when it was built by Robert Stevenson and his men, is now the oldest existing rock lighthouse in the British Isles.

'John Smeaton's tower on the Eddystone Rock had to be replaced last century. There was nothing wrong with the lighthouse itself but cracks were appearing in the rock on which it was built and of course that led to fears that the lighthouse itself might be undermined. The upper part of the tower was taken down and rebuilt on Plymouth Hoe where it still stands.'

A shaft of sunlight suddenly lit up the room. So intent had they both been on the story that neither of them had noticed that the rain had stopped.

'It looks as though it has cleared.' said Michael's grandfather. 'If you care to, we could take the binoculars and go for a walk along the cliffs. It is possible to get a good view of the lighthouse from there. You should be able to see it glinting in the sunshine.'

'I'll get my anorak.' Before the words were out of his mouth Michael was already through the living room door and halfway up the stairs.

His grandfather smiled and shook his head as he got up to put the fragment of stone from the Bell Rock back onto the shelf where it belonged. He, too, went out into the hall to collect his jacket.

As he lifted it down from the peg he laughed softly to himself. It might not be such a bad holiday for the boy after all.

APPENDIX

INCHCAPE ROCK
Robert Southey

No stir in the air, no stir in the sea,
The Ship was still as she could be;
Her sails from heaven recieved no motion,
Her keel was steady in the ocean.

Without either sign or sound of their shock,
The waves flow'd over the Inchcape Rock;
So little they rose, so little they fell,
They did not move the Inchcape Bell.

The Abbot of Aberbrothok
Had placed that bell on the Inchcape Rock;
On a buoy in the storm it floated and swung,
And over the waves its warning rung.

When the Rock was hid by the surge's swell,
The Mariners heard the warning Bell;
And then they knew the perilous rock,
And blest the Abbot of Aberbrothok.

The Sun in heaven was shining gay,
All things were joyful on that day;
The sea-birds scream'd as they wheel'd around,
And there was joyaunce in their sound.

The buoy of the Inchcape Bell was seen
A darker speck on the ocean green;
Sir Ralph the Rover walk'd his deck,
And fix'd his eye on the darker speck.

He felt the cheering power of spring,
It made him whistle, it made him sing;
His heart was mirthful to excess,
But the Rover's mirth was wickedness.

His eye was on the Inchcape Float;
Quoth he, "My men, put out the boat,
And row me to the Inchcape Rock,
And I'll plague the Abbot of Aberbrothock."

The boat is lower'd, the boatmen row,
And to the Inchcape Rock they go;
Sir Ralph bent over from the boat,
And he cut the Bell from the Inchcape Float.

Down sunk the Bell with a gurgling sound,
The bubbles rose and burst around;
Quoth Sir Ralph, "The next who comes to the Rock
Won't bless the Abbot of Aberbrothock."

Sir Ralph the Rover sail'd away,
He scour'd the seas for many a day;
And now grown rich with plunder'd store,
He steers his course for Scotland's shore.

So thick a haze o'erspreads the sky
They cannot see the sun on high;
The wind hath blown a gale all day,
At evening it hath died away.

On the deck the Rover takes his stand,
So dark it is they see no land.
Quoth Sir Ralph, "It will be lighter soon,
For there is the dawn of the rising Moon."

"Canst hear," said one, "the breakers roar?
For methinks we should be near the shore."
"Now, where we are I cannot tell,
But I wish we could hear the Inchcape Bell."

They hear no sound, the swell is strong;
Though the wind hath fallen they drift along,
Till the vessel strikes with a shivering shock,
"Oh Christ! It is the Inchcape rock!"

Sir Ralph the Rover tore his hair;
He curst himself in his despair;
The waves rush in on every side,
The ship is sinking beneath the tide.

But even in his dying fear
One dreadful sound could the Rover hear,
A sound as if with the Inchcape Bell,
The Devil below was ringing his knell.

1802

THE CHRONOLOGY OF
THE BELL ROCK LIGHTHOUSE

1786   The Commissioners of Northern Lights are appointed
        by Parliament to build four lighthouses in Scotland.

1787   The first of these lighthouses is set up at Kinnaird Head
        near Fraserburgh and begins operating on the 1st
        December, 1787.

1789   The success of the four lighthouses leads to demands
        for others to be built. Another Act is passed by
        Parliament extending the Lighthouse Board's authority
        to cover the whole of the Scottish coastline.

1793   It is suggested that a lighthouse should be built on the
        Bell Rock but nothing is done because of the
        difficulties and dangers involved.

1799   At the end of the year severe storms cause many
        shipping casualties around the Scottish coast. Pressure is
        again exerted to have a lighthouse built on the Bell
        Rock.

1800   In October, Robert Stevenson makes his first visit to
        the Rock. He draws up plans for a lighthouse there
        based on the Eddystone light and they are placed
        before the Commissioners.

1803   The first (unsuccessful) Bill enabling a lighthouse to be
        built on the Rock is brought before Parliament. In
        December H.M.S York is lost with all hands on the
        northeast coast of Scotland.

1804   The Lighthouse Board approach John Rennie to advise

on the many schemes suggested for a lighthouse on the Bell Rock. He agrees with Robert Stevenson in the type of construction required.

1806   A second, successful Bill granting finance for the building of the lighthouse is passed on the 16th July and preparatory work begins.

1807   The *Pharos,* or floating light, is towed to the Rock in July and becomes officially operational on the 15th September. In August the first workparty sets out for the Rock to build the beacon there. Before it is completed their lives are put at risk when the Smeaton goes adrift.

1808   Work presses ahead on the excavation of the foundation pit and the building of the railways to carry the stones. The construction of a cabin on the beacon begins and by the end of the working season the first three courses of masonry for the lighthouse are laid. A sailor is killed in an accident near the Rock.

1809   The workmen live in the cabin on the beacon but construction work is held up for ten days by a Government embargo on shipping. The first serious accident occurs to one of the men on the Rock and another is killed at the yard. In August the whole of the solid base of the lighthouse is completed.

1810   Plans are finalised on the form the lantern of the lighthouse is to take. Despite the severe frosts which affect work at the yard in the early months of the year, the rest of the tower is completed. In October one of the workmen is lost, presumed drowned.

1811   The lighthouse comes into operation on February 1st. In April John Forrest leaves the Rock after training the keepers but work continues on completing the interior of the house.

1813   The Signal Tower complex is completed.

1814   Sir Walter Scott visits the lighthouse with a party of Commissioners.

1815   Work begins on laying a stronger, permanent railway.

1816   The sloop *Smeaton* is replaced by a new tender *Pharos*.

1902   The original lighting apparatus is replaced by a new system using prisms, the first of a number of improvements made during the twentieth century.

1915   H.M.S. Argyll hits the Rock in October and sinks but all on board are rescued.

1955   An RAF helicopter crashes onto the Rock killing the crew and causing extensive damage to the lantern.

1988   The lighthouse is turned into an automatic light and officially demanned. It is now the oldest existing rock tower in the British Isles.

BIBLIOGRAPHY

M. Aitken, *Twelve Light Years,* Albyn Press, Haddington, East Lothian, 1988

K. Allardyce and E.M. Hood, *At Scotland's Edge,* Collins, London, 1986

W. Edwards, *Notes on European History, vol. 3, 1715 - 1815* Rivingtons, London, 1956

Encyclopaedia Britannica

D.B. Hague and R. Christie, *Lighthouses: Their Architecture, History and Archaeology,* Gomer Press, Llandysul, Dyfed, 1975

G. Hay, *History of Arbroath,* Arbroath, 1876

R.W. Munro, *Scottish Lighthouses,* Thule Press, Stornoway, 1979

T.C.Smout, *A History of the Scottish People 1560 - 1830,* Collins, London, 1969

S. Smiles, *Lives of the Engineers, vol. 2,* John Murray, London 1874

Robert Southey, *Minor Poems, vol.3,* London, 1815

Robert Stevenson, *An Account of the Bell Rock Lighthouse,* 1824

J. Stoddart, *Remarks on Scotland,* vol.1, London, 1801

INDEX